C000242876

Weapons and Equipment
of the Marlborough Wars

WEAPONS AND EQUIPMENT

OF THE

MARLBOROUGH WARS

ANTHONY KEMP

line illustrations by John Mollo

BLANDFORD PRESS

POOLE   DORSET

ACKNOWLEDGEMENTS

The authors and publishers wish to thank the following persons
and institutions for permission to reproduce illustrations from
their collections.

Courtauld Institute of Art, 1, 84.
Army Museums Ogilby Trust, 2, 42.
Department of the Environment, 3, 27, 28, 47.
Mollo Collection, 4, 5, 29, 48, 49, 65, 81, 85, 87.
Anne S. K. Brown Military Collection, Rhode Island, 6, 7, 8, 9,
    34, 35, 44, 45, 73, 82, 83, 88, 89, 93, 98, 99, 104, 105, 107.
National Army Museum, 10, 24, 25, 61, 62, 63, 64, 67, 92, 97,
    100.
The Duke of Marlborough, Blenheim Palace, 18, 22.
The Victoria & Albert Museum, 71, 79, 90, 91.
Sotheby's, 106.

First published in the U.K. 1980

British Library Cataloguing in Publication Data

Kemp, Anthony
    Weapons and equipment of the Marlborough wars.
    1. Arms and armour – Europe – History – 18th
    century
    I. Title
    623.4'094   U815

ISBN 0 7137 1013 6

Typeset and printed at
The Camelot Press Ltd, Southampton,
and bound by Robert Hartnoll Ltd, Bodmin, Cornwall

CONTENTS

Fig. 1. An equestrian portrait of John, 1st Duke of Marlborough. His armour was purely an artistic convention of the period and was never worn in battle.

INTRODUCTION

The title chosen for this book is perhaps somewhat misleading, but it was necessary to find something that would popularly identify a period in history. What better than to use the name of John Churchill, the first Duke of Marlborough. He was undoubtedly the finest soldier ever produced by England, as well as being a truly international figure known and admired throughout Europe during his lifetime. After all, we speak loosely of the 'Napoleonic era' to cover roughly the same time-span a century later. It is a fact of history that success breeds immortality on a grand scale, while lesser men like Wellington and Prince Eugene have only achieved fame in their respective countries.

Besides being an English duke who owed his earlier rise in society to the influence of a royal mistress and his lesser titles to court intrigue, Marlborough became a Prince of the Holy Roman Empire, Captain-General and Commander-in-Chief of a large Allied army. As a diplomat, he was empowered to conclude treaties on behalf of Queen Anne and her ministers, and during his period of power, functioned more or less as Foreign Secretary.

However, this book is not a biography of Marlborough, nor is it a history of his campaigns, sieges and battles. Its aim is to explain how his victories were achieved within the context of army organisation at the beginning of the eighteenth century – the human material, how this was organised and administered, and the weapons and equipment employed. All these factors are often ignored by military historians, and to understand weapons and equipment, one must also consider the armies that used them.

If we take the first fifteen years of the eighteenth century as our frame of reference, it is clear that the text mainly concerns the War of the Spanish Succession (1701–1714), but most of the detail could equally well apply to the roughly contemporary Great Northern War. Indeed, as far as the art of war was concerned, little was to change in Europe until the advent of the French Revolution towards the end of the century – bringing about the end of the 'Age of Enlightenment'.

The period around 1700 is of particular interest as it marks a radical change in the art of warfare, whereby the socket-bayonet finally replaced the pike. From then on, infantry firepower ruled the field of battle until the advent of armoured fighting vehicles in the twentieth century. There are, however, other factors, the chief one being the emergence of the 'modern' army as a disciplined force. Logistics as we know them today were not fully comprehended at the time and the necessary governmental back-up in terms of administration and finance was not really available. Marlborough's army, however, had ceased to be a marauding horde of starved predators. The troops under his direct control and influence were regularly fed and paid, the territories in which he operated were not totally devastated and the men had that intang-

1

ible commodity which we refer to today as high morale. Their victories proved that they were capable of heroic effort – within the limitations imposed by their weapons and equipment.

This has not been an easy book to compose, for the simple reason that the sources available to historians delving into later periods are almost entirely lacking. In the absence of laid-down standard patterns, regiments were equipped as their colonels' fancy took them, and the concept of 'uniformity' was only winning grudging acceptance. No consistent attempt was made to preserve the military artefacts of the period in museums, and apart from such solid items as firearms, the equipment has largely disappeared. What is available today is not a fully representative sample.

Failing the actual objects themselves recourse was had to contemporary sources wherever possible. We are lucky that a relatively large number of personal memoirs have come down to us from the War of the Spanish Succession, but these were not necessarily written for posterity – they are remarkable for what they left out as well as what they included. If you keep a diary today and refer to a 'bus journey into town, you assume that anyone reading it will know what a 'bus looks like and how many wheels it has.

Contemporary textbooks have also been consulted, but their particular problem is that they often represented wishful thinking rather than actual practice. The difficulty is to make really positive statements – to say that this or that item was used by a specific regiment on a specific date. I have also been able to draw on the research of others, notably the work of David Chandler, the most knowledgeable military historian of the eighteenth century.

The same factors apply to the illustrations. They are offered as samples and indications of weapons and equipment in use at the time, and much of the evidence on which they are based has been gleaned from paintings and engravings – in themselves often a dubious source. I have to state this disclaimer in case the 'uniform buffs' are tempted to tear me limb from limb.

Therefore the reader will find a number of generalisations and unsupported statements in the text – for which I make no apologies. There is simply not the information available and an increase in the scope of the text would have produced an unwieldy volume padded with further contradictions and 'might have beens'.

I could not have produced this book without the help of a number of individuals and organisations. My special thanks are due to H. L. Blackmore and Guy Wilson of the Tower Armouries; David Chandler; the Librarian of the Prince Consort's Library at Aldershot; and Dr Ernst Aichner of the Bavarian Army Museum. Other museums whose staff kindly devoted time to answer my queries were the National Army Museum, the Heeresgeschichtliches Museum in Vienna, and the Wehrgeschichtliche Museum in Rastatt.

Individuals who lent books and otherwise assisted include, Terry Gander, Ian Hogg, Dennis Quarmby, Herbert Jaeger and Philip Haythornthwaite. Finally, I owe a great debt to my collaborators – to Barry Gregory of Blandford Press for his unfailing help in this and other books, and to John Mollo who took time off from Outer Space to interpret my poor artistic efforts in such a capable way.

Anthony Kemp
Southampton, 1980

EARLY EIGHTEENTH-CENTURY ARMIES

Before studying their weapons and equipment in detail, it is worthwhile to consider briefly the armies that used them. Only thus can inanimate objects be placed in their true perspective. Artefacts lovingly displayed in museums and gorgeous uniforms pictured in glossy books were once used and worn by men engaged in the profession of arms. The collecting of such items, classified loosely as 'militaria' has become a popular pastime, but one must never overlook their original purpose – to aid a man in slaughtering his enemies.[1]

The underlying theme of the wars of the late seventeenth and early eighteenth centuries was an attempt by the Maritime Powers – England and Holland – to hinder French efforts towards the domination of Europe, inspired by the will of their monarch, Louis XIV.[2] If we accept that at the time Europe was the centre of the known world, then the War of the Spanish Succession, together with the roughly contemporary Great Northern War, was truly a world conflict. In the former struggle, France, allied with Bavaria and the 'legitimate' King of Spain, was confronted by England, Holland, the motley forces of the Empire and their allies among the German princes. Savoy changed horses in midstream. In the latter war, Sweden was up against the emergent power of Russia under Peter the Great. Besides the traditional European theatres of war in Flanders, Poland and on the Danube, the conflicts extended into the Iberian peninsula, North America and the plains of Hungary where the Empire had to contend with local rebellion. Only the Turks were quiescent, licking their wounds after the defeats suffered at the hands of Prince Eugene of Savoy in 1697 and 1698.

The wars of the Baroque age are often termed 'dynastic' in that they were fought to achieve the ends of various ruling houses, as well as being 'limited' in scope. It is true that there was no real ideology involved, and as a result of general revulsion at the excesses committed in the name of religion during the Thirty Years War, the tendency was for small professional armies. The real limitation to warfare, however, was not imposed by the political or moral restraints, but was influenced to a far greater extent by logistics. No state at the time had the resources to put large armies into the field and to keep them there.

All the European armies of the period were organised and equipped along basically the same lines. Except for the republican Dutch, they were all nominally subject to a monarch who in turn incorporated in his or her person the sense of nation or state. Only in England had a sense of constitutional monarchy subject to control by Parliament evolved. Other monarchs were in theory 'absolute' in that they were not subject to the will of elected assemblies or estates. The France of Louis XIV (and slightly later, the Prussia of Frederick the Great) was the prime example of absolute monarchy, and other powers usually faced restrictions of one form or another in their exercise of government. The war effort of the House of Hapsburg, for example, could only be financed by contributions from the Estates of the hereditary lands — who were basically unwilling to pay up. Hence the need for subsidies from the Maritime Powers to keep the Imperial armies in the field.

Another and better classification for Baroque warfare is provided by Professor Michael Howard who used the term 'The Wars of the Professionals',[3] for that is what armies had become by 1700, growing throughout the sixteenth and seventeenth centuries from the old unruly feudal hordes. The officers were no longer part of a pan-European warrior clique fighting out of a sense of feudal obligation, or mercenary contractors providing armed men to whoever could pay for them. In fact, the bulk of the 'officer class' in Europe had become civil servants — of the state which employed and (in theory at least) paid them on a regular basis in peace and war.

This was not something that had happened suddenly, and most officers were still a quarrelsome lot acting according to a well-defined code of honour. Slights could only be avenged by recourse to the duel, as is emphasised by many of the memoirs of the period, and it was still possible to change sides during the course of a war — provided that such a step could be justified on a point of honour. If a humble soldier took the same step, he was a deserter who was liable to be strung up without further ado. The Comte de Mérode-Westerloo, a Fleming, transferred from Spanish to French service and then crossed over to the Empire during the War of the Spanish Succession.

Many English officers were still torn by loyalty to the 'king over the water', the Old Pretender, and even Marlborough had to make the decision to desert his royal patron, James II, and transfer his allegiance to William III in 1688. Governments often had to struggle with proud noblemen who resented any form of civilian interference into military affairs, and it was only gradually that the royal cipher replaced the arms of the colonel proprietors on regimental colours and equipment.

In most European countries, however, by 1700, basic state machinery had been created for the purposes of maintaining armed forces on a standing basis, and capable in theory of arming, clothing, paying and feeding them. These armies thus tended to become separate societies with their own laws and customs, separated from civilian life by dress, manners and outlook.

Without the establishment of state bureaucracies, such paid forces would have been impossible, and conversely, the increase in the technical complexity of war made such organisations essential. At the same time, armed forces could be used by a government as an instrument of coercion in the effort to gain even more power over the lives of its citizens. This in turn led to the mobilisation of even greater resources which paved the way for the maintenance of even larger standing armies.

It was the very threat posed to society in England by the Catholic regiments of James II, and folk-memories of Cromwell's major-generals, that stiffened Parliamentary dislike of standing armies after 1688. If they were a necessary evil, then they had to be kept as small as possible, and after every war, to be swiftly reduced.

With regard to England, it has to be borne in mind that her island position has given the English immunity from the more or less perpetual warfare that has been the lot of countries on the Continent since time immemorial. Out of sheer necessity, it was the United Provinces with their republican constitution, fighting for their survival against Spain in the early part of the seventeenth century, who took the lead in forming a professional army. Indeed, one could go as far as to say that it was the influence of Protestantism, taking root in northern Europe, that made this possible in the first place; the very essence of a professional army is discipline, which blends well with the sober and orderly doctrines of Luther and Calvin. The Dutch with their income from trade were in a position to maintain standing forces and pay their troops regularly — in return for which they could demand obedience. This sobering Protestant influence applied equally to the Swedish, the New Model and the Brandenburg/Prussian armies.

Discipline was required, for the simple reason that developments in tactics made it essential. As battlefield evolutions were discovered and improved upon, and as firearms came to be used in increasing numbers, so drill became necessary. Great commanders like Maurice of Nassau and Gustavus Adolphus realised this, and their armies were successful because they were disciplined and well drilled. Marlborough was no great tactical innovator. He took the forces and systems that he inherited and made the best use of them, refining their tactics in the light of experience and introducing the concept of regular training. How much he actually achieved, however, must remain a matter for conjecture.

The key to the development of 'modern' armies is to be found in the Sweden of Gustavus Adolphus, where feudalism had never become really established. When he was killed in battle in 1632, he had built up an army of some 140,000 men officered by the nobility and levied under a concept of national military service. Only one man in ten who was eligible was called to the colours, while the rest were taxed to pay for his equipment. Sweden, however, was a small country in terms of population, and for his campaigns in Germany, Gustavus had to rely on contingents of mercenaries. On account of the religious motive, service in his army was popular among Protestants, and many of the commanders on both sides of the English Civil War learnt their trade under him or in the Dutch army.

The Swedish army could only point the way, and the system collapsed on the death of the king. More in the way of state control of resources was needed if armies were to be transformed from half starved mobs into disciplined entities. Without this, no orderly state system was possible, but first, the machinery had to be created.

During the latter part of the seventeenth cen-tury, the power vacuum that ensued after the Thirty Years War was filled by France, emerging under Louis XIV from a long period of civil and religious strife. Her armies came to be feared throughout Europe and her military systems had to be emulated by those who were threatened if they wanted to survive. This pinnacle of power was in fact created within a remarkably short space of time, guided by the supreme will of Louis. As a young man he had had personal experience of the evils of aristocratic faction, and he inherited a bankrupt and divided country riddled with corruption. Coming to the throne in 1660, he determined to finally break the power of the great noble families, but to do so he had to find them an outlet for their talents.

For his advisers, Louis tended to select men from the rising bourgeois classes who owed positions solely to royal favour – thus providing a guarantee of their loyalty. The perfect instruments for the furtherance of his military ambitions he found in le Tellier and his son who became the Marquis de Louvois. Under their guidance the armed forces of the crown numbered 300,000 men by 1680, but even they, backed by full royal support, had great difficulties in overcoming centuries of inertia and entrenched vested interests. It was not simply a matter of tightening control of the army itself. First, the resources had to be found to pay for it, but again, the right man was at hand. Under Colbert, the crown became a patron of trade and industry with a commensurate increase in royal revenues.

Realising his limitations, Louvois left the colonel proprietors in control of their regiments, and responsible for such matters as payment and recruiting, but the King appointed the lieutenant-colonels who would command them in action. To oversee the activities of the colonels, royal agents were attached as inspectors to ensure that the king got value for his money. Above regimental level, a vast bureaucracy was set up to administer army affairs, an unheard of thing in a period when state offices were normally regarded as saleable commodities or rewards to be given to court favourites.

The *intendance* had originated earlier under Richelieu, but the le Telliers expanded it into a tight organisation of inspectors attached to the field armies, supervising equipment, pay and provisioning. They oversaw all contracts and influenced virtually every aspect of military life, much to the disgust of professional officers, but the population as a whole preferrred this to an army living off the country. Today, accustomed as we are to state intervention into virtually every aspect of our lives, it is clear that the *intendance* was far from perfect and that corruption naturally continued to flourish. It did, however, establish a standard practice to be emulated throughout Europe – with differing amounts of success!

The worst organised armies of the period were those of the Hapsburg rulers of Austria. The bulk of the funds to pay for the upkeep of soldiers had to be extorted from unwilling provincial Estates, and expenditure never met up with income. Lacking a competent civil service, the government had to fall back on the services of civilian contractors (mainly Jewish), which it was mostly incapable of paying. Bankruptcies were frequent in this risky form of commercial enterprise. Some attempts were made to improve the system when Prince Eugene became President of the Imperial War Council, but the basic inertia of court politics defeated even that great soldier.

The most important strides were made in the distant German electorate based on the sandy heathlands around Berlin, which was to become the Kingdom of Prussia at the beginning of the eighteenth century. A docile peasant population, solidly Protestant, was welded together under a number of able monarchs into the most formidable military machine that Europe had ever known. During the period with which we are concerned, Frederick William I was laying the foundations of the army that was to be exploited by his son Frederick the Great – who inherited a full treasury and an army of 80,000 men.

The backbone of the Prussian army was the officer corps, recruited almost entirely from the impoverished lesser nobility under a system of virtual conscription. Under the so-called social compact, they were obliged to serve the state in return for royal confirmation of their privileges and even to send their sons to the cadet academies. Realising that theirs was a poor country, successive monarchs took steps to mobilise resources to finance their army – with a thoroughness that was to become so typical of the Hohenzollern state. The middle classes were exempt from service, but in return, bore the main weight of taxation and royal control of commerce and industry. The troops were recruited partly from among the peasantry, but preferably from footloose foreigners serving for the money – so as not to disturb local agriculture.

The other armies from the German principalities and electorates, mainly aped French traditions in the matter of dress, equipment and organisation. Apart from the Bavarians, who backed the wrong horse by supporting France, the rest of them supported the Allied cause, hiring out their troops for English and Dutch gold.[4]

In keeping with development of the parliamentary traditions, the organisation of the English army evolved along somewhat different lines, but the end product was basically the same as on the Continent. The regular army as we know it today grew from the household troops permitted to Charles II under the Restoration settlement, but in a link with the past, the 2nd Foot Guards (now the Coldstream Guards) were a remnant of the New Model Army still serving under General Monck. Nominally, the soldiers were the King's (or Queen's) but the monarch could not and did not pay them – to keep an army in the field he or she had to go before Parliament. The only standing troops permitted were carried under the heading of 'guards and garrisons' in peacetime. These were the royal guard regiments, both horse and foot, certain ordinary regiments and the garrisons of the coastal fortresses. As an additional complication, many of those employed in the latter were civilian gunners belonging to the Board of Ordnance and paid from different funds.

Looking more closely at English military administration, it soon became clear that there was often no real dividing line between military and civilian — what administration there was had largely evolved by custom and trial and error over the preceding centuries. The fact was that the England of Queen Anne was in a state of political flux and the country was rent by factional strife — the battle between Whig and Tory further complicated by tastes in religion and loyalty to the exiled Stuarts. It was generally recognised that an army was a necessary evil, but which in turn became involved in domestic politics. The fall of Marlborough, bedchamber intrigues and the English desertion of her Allies were all part of the broad sweep of home affairs.

One problem was that a whole number of ministers and committees could exert influence upon army affairs and no 'correct channels of communication' were laid down — a situation abhorrent to any modern soldier. Thus complaints could often go over the head of a commander in the field and were decided frequently by court intrigue and political influence.

Within the royal council or cabinet at the time of Queen Anne, there were two secretaries of state, responsible for the North and South geographically. They were in theory responsible for deciding the number of troops required, appointing suitable officers to command them and determining where they should be used. These men were the Queen's ministers and not necessarily from a majority party in Parliament, but had to justify their activities to that body. Of equal importance was the Lord Treasurer, who was responsible for finding the money to maintain the army and for doling it out as and when it became available. Marlborough was fortunate in that during his campaigns, his friend Lord Godolphin was in charge of the Treasury.

During the reign, however, another figure grew in importance – the Secretary at War who earlier had been purely the secretary of the Commander-in-Chief. Much of the routine army correspondence was routed through his office, and by the end of the reign he tended to be the official link between the cabinet and the army commanders in the field. As a politician, he gave Parliament by virtue of his office, a certain influence in army affairs, whereas previously, they had tended to regard the army as an unwelcome extension of the royal prerogative.

The legal basis for any army at all lay in the Mutiny Acts which were passed from time to time. Their ostensible purpose was to define purely military crime and to authorise punishment, but could contain restraining provisions that were binding on the Crown and its ministers.

When the Spanish Succession War broke out in 1701, there were less than 8,000 troops in England — not counting the separate Irish and Scottish establishments. We had a treaty commitment to provide 10,000 men to aid our Dutch allies, but in a sudden spirit of generosity, Parliament voted 40,000 troops for Flanders. Of these, only some 18,000 were to be Subject Troops (i.e. Subjects of the Queen), while the rest were to be made up by hiring from the German princes. In view of the subsequent scale of the war, Parliament was then persuaded to vote a further 20,000, 3,000 of whom were Subject Troops, and the cost was to be split with the Dutch (the so-called Flanders augmentation).

The term Flanders covered all of Europe except for the Peninsula where separate arrangements prevailed. Although at one time 34,000 subject troops were voted, it is unlikely that there were ever more than 15,000 actually serving overseas.[5]

ORGANISATION IN THE FIELD

Although the army corps and the division in the modern sense did not exist at the time, it was clear that Marlborough's army was far too large and unwieldy to be controlled by one man. Broadly speaking, the field army was divided into two wings and formed up for battle in two

Fig. 2. The Battle of Blenheim. Attributed to James Ross.

lines, plus reserves forming a third. The infantry and cavalry of both wings were commanded separately and could thus be equated to an army corps. The lines themselves were sub-divided into brigades, but these were tactical rather than administrative groupings.[6] Each wing had a lieutenant-general of horse and a lieutenant-general of foot. The brigadiers often tended to be the commanding officers of regiments within their brigades. Besides these tactical elements, the army could be split on the march. On the way to the Danube, Marlborough retained with him the cavalry, and sent the foot and the artillery by a different route, commanded by his brother, General Churchill.

In theory, the monarch was the Commander-in-Chief of the English army, but when he (or she) did not exercise command in person, this task was delegated. Queen Anne appointed her husband, Prince George of Denmark, as Lord High Admiral and Generalissimo of all Her Land Forces, but luckily he was content with these sonorous titles. Real control was vested in Marlborough as Captain-General. His appointment gave him considerable powers of strategic direction of the war, but he was not allowed to raise troops and had no control over funds or stores. In addition, the Dutch appointed him as Allied Commander-in-Chief, although their field deputies constantly hampered his powers of decision. Besides his purely field responsibilities, he acted as England's roving ambassador and was the Master General of the Ordnance, thus being able to exert considerable influence on the provision of artillery and engineer services.

To assist him in his many tasks he had a ridiculously small staff – by present-day standards. In the field, the Captain-General was accompanied by a number of government

Fig. 3. The Battle of Blenheim by Laguerre. Marlborough and his staff are in the foreground.

representatives over whom he had no direct control. The Judge-Advocate-General was a civilian official responsible for the legal powers of the Crown, and dealt with such matters as the administration of justice, courts-martial and other legal affairs. The Treasury was represented by the Paymaster-General who issued money to the regiments and had a staff of paymasters and clerks. As Marlborough was Master-General, it seems that the Board of Ordnance had no official representative at his headquarters as had been the custom previously.

As usual it is difficult to be dogmatic about the personal staff of the Captain-General. His principal assistant was his Quartermaster-General, traditionally responsible for such matters as scouting the route of march and for selecting and setting up camp sites. Cadogan, however, functioned in the same way as a modern Chief-of-Staff to Marlborough, at times even exercising independent command and being responsible for intelligence matters. Next in the 'inner circle' was Cardonnel, the Duke's secretary, who took care of the mass of correspondence emanating from headquarters. There were two Adjutant-Generals who also had

purely administrative duties and may well have been attached to the two wings as liaison officers. A Deputy Judge-Advocate dealt with legal affairs, and the Waggon-Master-General was responsible for the movement of the army and the provision of transport. Medical matters were handled by the Surgeon-General, Physician-General and the Apothecary-General, while Marlborough's spiritual welfare was in the hands of his Chaplain, Dr Hare. The Provost-Marshal-General was responsible for the administration of justice, the execution of sentences as well as camp discipline and organisation.

It is interesting to note that most of these staff titles are still in use in the modern army.

In addition to the above office holders, there were a number of aides-de-camp whose main duty was to transmit the orders of the Captain-General during battle. They were mounted and probably held the rank of captain. Tapestries and portraits show the Duke always accompanied by a number of mounted dignitaries, as a great man could always attract a following. Besides the staff, there were the representatives of the Dutch States-General and foreign dignitaries such as the German princes whose troops were under his command. His artillery and engineering advisers were also probably in attendance at times, and visitors such as Prince Eugene or the Margrave of Baden would have brought their own retinues with them.

At a lower level, the staff would have been filled out by a number of clerks as well as the servants, valets, cooks and other menials attached to the high-ranking officers. Finally, it is known that Marlborough employed a number of runners for carrying messages. As they do not feature on any official establishments, nothing is known about their status or rank. They can be seen on some of the tapestries, dressed in blue short coats, breeches, stocking and jockey caps. As their symbol of authority they carried brass-headed staves, similar in size and shape to the baton of a drum-major.

One can assume that some forty people clustered around Marlborough in camp and on the march, but of these, only Cadogan, Cardonnel and Dr Hare seem to have enjoyed his confidence to the extent that they dined regularly in his tent.

THE OFFICERS

In most European armies of the period, commissions were reserved for the nobility and gentry. In some countries where there were large numbers of those regarded as being of noble birth, this was simple, but in England with its relatively small numbers of aristocracy, the distinctions were far more subtle. To be an officer you had to be a gentleman – technically someone who had the right to a coat of arms. However, if a man behaved like a gentleman and had the necessary influence or powers of persuasion, he could become an officer without too many questions being asked.

In French and Prussian service, commissions were reserved for the 'noblesse', most of whom would have been regarded simply as gentry in England. Many of the higher commands were filled by Princes of the Blood as of right, which

led to problems when men of lower social standing were placed above them in command. The Baroque age was one where precedence and birth were all-important in civilian life, a tendency which naturally transferred itself to the army. Exceptions were possible, however, as the base-born could achieve officer status in the artillery and engineers – arms of the service which were not regarded as being socially acceptable or occupations fit for a gentleman.

Even Marlborough himself suffered from these problems. As an English Duke he ranked far lower in Europe than a Sovereign Prince, but by virtue of his offices, he found himself in command of his social superiors. In an attempt to avoid this anomaly and as a reward for services rendered after Blenheim, the Emperor invested him with the title of Prince of Mindelheim, thus giving him the status of a prince of the Holy Roman Empire.

Motives for joining the army naturally differed. Under a famous commander, prestige could be gained, which naturally attracted the high nobility – at times the whole French Court went off on campaign complete with mistresses, musicians and all the comforts of Versailles. On the other hand, the bulk of the officer class in all the armies of the period was made up from the second sons of the gentry, not particularly well off, who regarded the army as a decent way of making a sort of living. Many were rakes, drinkers and duellists attracted to the army by the prospects of roistering and loot, but at the opposite end of the scale we have Colonel Blackader of the Cameronians, as solemn a Presbyterian Scot as ever produced by the Kirk.

The rank structure in English service was generally similar to modern practice, with generals, lieutenant-generals, major-generals and brigadiers occupying the higher commands, many of whom would also be colonels of regiments at the same time. All were appointed in theory by the Crown and it was the Queen who signed their commissions. In practice, however, both patronage and selection by the Captain-General played a decisive role. During the early days of power and influence,

Marlborough had a virtually free hand in the selection of senior officers, but as his prestige at home waned, he had to suffer more and more interference from politicians and court intrigue.

In most of the continental armies, senior appointments were strictly controlled by the various monarchs. The career of an officer in French service was determined by the Louvois bureaucracy directly responsible to the King.

At the lower end of the scale, virtually all officers owed their appointment and promotion to purchase, often combined with patronage or family influence. A young man with a mind for a career in Queen Anne's army started off by purchasing a commission as cornet or ensign — for which he required no formal military qualifications other than being regarded as a gentleman. His progress was then determined by his purse as he bought his way up the ladder, or he could hope for promotion in the field to vacancies caused by death or disability.

In theory, buying and selling commissions was illegal, but it was a practice that was universally recognised in England. Marlborough and many of his contemporaries supported it as a way of reducing the cost of the army. Only the most frugal officer could expect to live on his pay, and in theory, the purchase system ensured that only men of means came into the army. It also had the virtue that it freed military appointments at regimental level from undue Parliamentary control.

There were standard recognised charges, higher for the more prestigious regiments, and the commission once owned became an insurance policy for old age, as it could be sold on retirement. The fact that purchase was condoned can be seen from the proviso that 12 pence out of every pound paid for a commission had to be made over to the Royal Hospital at Chelsea. A man receiving promotion to fill a vacancy in the field, might well have been required to make a payment to the widow of the dead officer.

One problem was that although technically an army career was only open to a man of means, it was not an attractive one to the really wealthy — with the result that many officers of slender means were tempted to increase their pay via corruption and downright fraud.

As far as punishment was concerned, the worst that could befall an officer was to be imprisoned or cashiered, and even in such extreme cases he was usually permitted to sell his commission. The usual offences were misappropriation of funds or other financial misdemeanours, but absenteeism was a perennial curse. There was no such thing as official leave scales and officers were expected to take time off during the winter months when campaigning was impossible. Often, however, they were simply absent from their posts and it seems that little could be done to stop this — especially in the case of unpopular stations such as Ireland, the West Indies and the Peninsula. An added dimension was the fact that officers promoted to general rank liked to retain their regimental commands and companies, thus continuing to draw the pay, and the practice of granting commissions to children. This was not widespread and was certainly not officially encouraged, but did occur.[7]

Once commissioned, an officer was expected to provide himself with a suitable outfit according to his status. For a subaltern of foot, this could mean his basic uniform and equipment (sword, spontoon and/or musket), tent, camp furniture, crockery, cutlery, bedding, etc. Quite a large capital sum was required, and as promotion was gained, an officer was expected to increase the amount of baggage with which he campaigned.

Thus Marlborough's officers were a pretty mixed bunch who, under an incompetent commander, could soon get out of hand. The cowards by and large made themselves scarce fairly rapidly, as service in the field provided a system of natural selection. The incompetents were weeded out or got themselves killed — on occasions by their own men.[8] Those that remained were undoubtedly brave men in the context of their code of honour which rated courage very highly, although many had no

11

Fig. 4. Early eighteenth-century recruiting scene. Note the servant pouring a drink. Engraving after E. Ridinger.

real professional training. For all their drunkenness, petty quarrels and swaggering bravado, their ornate dress and flowing wigs, they seemed to have been able to inspire respect and lead the motley crews of soldiers placed under them – all for niggardly pay, extreme discomfort and the sure knowledge that when the war was over, they would end up on the scrap-heap of half-pay doled out by an ungrateful government.

THE SOLDIERS

The pay and conditions of service in early eighteenth century armies were not calculated to inspire readiness to enlist, and recruitment and desertion were the two main problems confronting any commanding officer. First he had to find the men and then keep them.

As the colonel was the owner of his regiment, it followed that his capital and stock-in-trade were his soldiers – without them he could not operate his 'business' of providing troops, and thus his potential profits would disappear. The same factors also applied to the company

which was owned by the captain. One must bear in mind, however, that the establishments laid down in official documents often represented wishful thinking on the part of the authorities, and most units in any army were permanently under strength. Various practices were indulged in. In the English army each company was allowed one or two 'widows' men' whose pay was expected to provide for the dependants of those killed in action, while some unscrupulous officers enrolled their servants as privates to pocket the pay themselves. To cover up deficiencies in the mustered numbers, men could be induced for a small sum to stand in for missing men on parade – who were known as 'faggots' in contemporary slang.

Apparently it proved fairly easy to raise new units. A prominent person would be granted the right to raise a regiment by the Crown, and it would thereafter bear his name as long as he remained actually or nominally in command. Once the regiment was on the strength, it was the colonel's responsibility to keep the numbers up to scratch.

The underlying problem was that the govern-

Fig. 5. French conscripts drawing lots to determine those who had to serve. Anon. drawing, 1688.

ment had authorised an army greater than could be maintained by the recruiting system and as serious conscription was never resorted to in England during the War of the Spanish Succession, the situation worsened from year to year as the conflict extended beyond the scope of an annual campaign in Flanders.

Apart from the obvious factor of wastage in battle, there were the ever present problems of desertion and disease. The latter was a vital factor in the West Indies where the troops died literally like flies from tropical diseases, and the mortality rate on the troopships to the Peninsula was horrific. In extreme cases only a third of the men embarked finally reached their regiments.[9]

The normal system was that when regiments retired into their allotted winter quarters, they sent recruiting parties back to the British Isles, usually consisting of an officer, a sergeant and a drummer – who had to be prepared to use every trick in the book to get their quota of men.

Luckily we have a good picture of contemporary recruiting methods in the play *The Recruiting Sergeant* by George Farquhar, which was first produced on the London stage in 1706. It is even more valuable as evidence when one considers that the author knew what he was writing about. Farquhar had been commissioned a Lieutenant of Grenadiers in Orrery's Regiment, and spent parts of 1705 and 1706 recruiting in Lichfield and Shrewsbury.

Good, the play is a comedy. However, it was popular right from the start and thus its theme must have been a valid one to those who saw it. The subject was undoubtedly exaggerated – for comic effect – but the picture it presented of recruiting methods cannot have been too wide of the mark. The following is part of Sergeant Kite's speech which opens the play:

'If any gentlemen soldiers or others have a mind to serve her Majesty and pull down the French King, if any 'prentices have severe masters, any children have undutiful parents, if any servants have too little wages, or any husband too much wife, let them repair to the noble Sergeant Kite at the Sign of the Raven in this good town of Shrewsbury and they shall receive present relief and entertainment.'

The 'relief and entertainment' was in the form of strong drink, a powerful inducement, but once the sergeant had beat his drum, his problems were far from over. Catholics were naturally barred from service, and those who did volunteer were hardly the cream of society. All that Sergeant Kite managed to entice were 'the strong man of Kent, the King of the Gypsies, a Scotch pedlar, a Scoundrel Attorney and a Welsh parson' – in the space of a week. His superior, Captain Plume, ordered him to get rid of the Scoundrel Attorney as he would not have men in his company who could read or write – as they were too adroit at drawing up petitions.

Therefore there had to be a pecuniary inducement. We think of the term 'the King's shilling', but during the reign of Anne, the going rate was £2 – a vast sum of money for an unskilled man. This meant that with his levy money, clothing and equipment, a recruit represented a considerable investment to the colonel of a regiment.

Thus, once they had been cajoled or tricked into joining the army, the unfortunate wretches were more often than not treated as prisoners until they could be herded on to the transports for Flanders or Spain. However, not all the trickery was on the side of the recruiting parties, and in some cases there was a very real need for close confinement. The high inducement offered naturally led to 'professional' recruits enlisting for the money and then promptly deserting to join the next regiment as soon as the opportunity presented itself. This was all too easy in the absence of any central documentation, and besides, recruiting parties seldom asked awkward questions. The 'Amiable Renegade', Peter Drake, enlisted in a number of regiments all at the same time, in search of a better deal in the way of promotion better suited to his imagined station in society.

In the absence of a concept of general conscription and in spite of the efforts of hundreds of Sergeant Kites, there remained a vast manpower gap to be filled. As a result, resort was had to impressment and other dubious practices. One measure was to release debtors from prison if they were prepared to enlist. This was embodied in an Act of Parliament in 1701 but was an open invitation to corruption. The debtors were prepared to promise anything to get out of prison, but many had absconded when the time came to embark.

The same Act provided for the enlistment of sentenced criminals, including capital offenders. One must bear in mind that at the time a man could be hung for a comparatively trivial offence, but the armies were certainly filled out with a leavening of gallows birds – even the army was preferable to Tyburn!

In addition, the Justices of the Peace were empowered to forcibly enlist able-bodied men with 'no lawful calling or visible means of support', and parish constables were made responsible for such levies. This was nothing new as a method of raising troops, but it did create problems. The Act had to be sufficiently amended to prohibit the impressment of harvest workers during the summer months as otherwise agriculture would have suffered.

Once the men had been enlisted by whatever method, they were transported off to wherever their new regiments were stationed. There they were kitted out, often in the clothes taken from their dead predecessors, and put through a crash course of drill. The camp regulations stipulated that recruits were to exercise during the afternoons with 'small cartouches'. In the absence of officially laid down training programmes, it would seem that the amount of instruction given depended largely on the attitude of officers and nco's of individual units. The unlucky recruits were those who arrived in the middle of a campaigning season who could well have found themselves in combat within a few days.

It is probable that this very point must have caused problems, as it was after the Spanish Succession War that numbers of drill manuals and treatises started to appear in English. Certainly the army as a whole was not drilled in peace-time, probably on account of Parliamentary fears of large assemblies of armed men. The Camp on Hounslow Heath in the reign of James II was not repeated, with all its undertones of Popish hordes being used to subdue the loyal Commons. It was the threat of Napoleon a century later that led to Sir John Moore's training schemes being officially approved.

The above remarks applied naturally to the English army, but other countries had different systems. The high standard of drill for which the Prussian army later became famous, first really got underway after 1715 when Leopold, Prince of Anhalt-Dessau took charge of army reforms. The French army certainly led the way in terms of general training and the systems laid down under the guidance of Louvois specified regular exercises at regimental level and while in garrison. In addition, large peacetime manoeuvres were organised, attended by the court in all its panoply, and the bulk of military textbooks of the period were written by Frenchmen.

To sum up, one can assume that the standard of training in the élite standing regiments was probably fairly high, but as most armies recruited the bulk of their troops only in wartime, the ordinary line regiments of horse and foot had to muddle along as best they could. Under these circumstances, what was remarkable was the endurance of early eighteenth-century armies on campaign, composed as they were of the dregs of society, poorly fed and equipped, and subjected to draconian discipline.

DISCIPLINE AND MORALE

As a final section to this brief survey of army organisation in the Marlborough period, a word must be said about discipline – without which no army could have functioned. Military treatises of the period are full of engravings of scenes showing the infliction of punishment, and when one considers the social make-up of the ranks, it is clear that a deterrent system of punishment was needed. Many schemes of camp layouts featured a gallows as a matter of course, but these may have been designed as a deterrent symbol of the power of military justice.

The legal basis of martial law naturally varied from country to country and often depended upon the organisational state of the army concerned. In many cases, officers and nco's were permitted to strike their men with their canes or halberds. In the more aristocratic armies, it is clear that commanding officers had powers to punish without being accountable to any superior body. In Bavarian service, de la Colonie could apparently discipline his grenadier regiment as he thought fit.

In the more legalistic English army, such matters were fairly strictly regulated, although summary justice was meted out on occasion. The basis of military law was established in the Mutiny Acts, which formed the framework for the Articles of War laid down by the Commander-in-Chief.[10] These were read to all recruits on enlistment and also to the army from time to time. They listed the various military offences, such as desertion, plundering, abandoning one's post, assaulting superiors, etc., and laid down the punishments to be meted out.

Overall supervision of military justice was exercised by the Judge-Advocate-General, a legal official appointed by the government. The Provost-Marshal-General was responsible for the custody of offenders and for the supervision of sentences. It is worth quoting from Mother Ross regarding his activities:

'As some of my readers may not know the Provost's office, it will not be amiss to tell them that he attends camp, and all offenders are put under his care, for which reason he commands a strong guard which goes everywhere with him; and the camp colour-men who always precede

Fig. 6. Engraving of a camp scene showing a soldier running the gauntlet. N. Guerard, circa 1700. Fig. 7. The Wooden Horse. In this French engraving, the figure on the right would appear to be a woman. N.Guerard.

the army, escorted by the forlorn-hope, choose the strongest house they can meet with for his quarters, that he may secure his prisoners. When we march, the lesser criminals are hand-cuffed in the middle of a guard; but the notorious ones are chained hand and foot, and put into the bread waggons.'[11]

Prior to 1680, the Provost had had a representative at regimental level, but his duties were then taken over by the Quartermaster. The actual infliction of punishment was the responsibility of the drummers.

General and Regimental Courts-Martial heard cases and handed down sentences. Capi-

Fig. 8. Scene in a cavalry camp with a trooper standing on a very mild form of picquet. The men on the left seem to be playing a game. N.Guerard.

Fig. 9. Guard mounting in a Prussian barracks. Note the Wooden Horse and the picquet. Engraving in Fleming, Der Volkommene Deutsche Soldat, *1726.*

tal offences could only be tried by the former, while the latter could only award corporal punishment. There is no evidence to suggest that large scale executions were carried out in the English army at the time, although hanging was a commonplace event at home. Marlborough frequently threatened to hang men caught plundering, and obviously some suffered 'to encourage the others'. Desertion was normally punished by shooting 'at the head of the regiment'.

Lesser forms of punishment seem to have been generally similar throughout Europe. Flogging by being tied to a frame made of halberds was the most popular, but for more serious crimes, running the gauntlet was used.

The offender had to run between two files of men who belaboured the unfortunate wretch with sticks. The Wooden Horse had a back made of two boards which met at an acute angle. The offender had to sit on this with his legs weighted down for a number of hours which must have caused extreme discomfort. The artillery version of this was for the prisoner to sit astride a gun. The cavalry used picqueting, whereby the offender had to stand on a stool while his right hand was fastened above him to a ring in the wall or post. When the stool was removed, his feet rested on two pointed stakes driven into the ground. While suspended there, he could also be whipped.

All this may sound barbaric, but flogging was retained until well into the nineteenth century in the British army, and No. 1 Field Punishment, often resorted to during the First World War, was hardly less barbaric than the Wooden Horse.[12]

Apart from the purely criminal offences, the Articles of War defined a number of crimes of a moral nature. Articles 1–5 were concerned with such matters as suttling during Divine Service, blasphemy, oaths, execrations, assaulting chaplains and profaning places of worship. Protestant sobriety was still strong in the England of the time, but soldiers are the same the world over. Anyone who has served in the Forces well knows the ripe vocabulary of blasphemy and mighty oaths which form the language of any training depot nco.

Colonel Blackader spends most of his diary in castigating the morals of the troops, and the following extract is but a brief sample:

'. . . for I had the offscourings of the garrison with me, both officers and soldiers, most abominable vermin whom my soul abhors. O Lord, how long shall I dwell among men whose tongues are set on fire of hell! O, when wilt Thou deliver me out of this horrid and noisesome company? My mind chafed and vexed the whole day by villainy and abominations of all sorts, both against the laws of God and man. Cursing, swearing, drunkenness, robbing, thieving, mutiny etc.'[13]

In spite of the rolling Old Testament language of Blackader, the soldiers of the early eighteenth century were probably no better and no worse than at any other time, whereby the worst crime is to be caught. Harsh discipline has always failed to produce high morale or stamp out crime. We do know that Marlborough was highly regarded by his men as a commander who looked after their interests, and in spite of many individual lapses, they were far better disciplined than Wellington's troops, for example.

NOTES

Only the name of the author is given where reference is made to books listed in the bibliography, except where the same author has written two or more books cited.

1 For a more detailed review of armies at the beginning of the eighteenth century, the reader is recommended to consult Fortescue and Scouller.
2 I use the term 'England' purposely throughout, as it was employed consciously by contemporary writers. The Act of Union with Scotland was passed in 1707.
3 Howard. 54.
4 Some sample treaties are quoted in Trevelyan. *Select Documents.* pp. 2–15.
5 Scouller. 91.
6 Atkinson. 8n.
7 Scouller. 277.
8 Chandler. *Art of War.* 106n.
9 Scouller. 120.
10 Ibid. Appendix J.
11 Defoe. *Life and Adventures.*
12 No. 1 Field Punishment consisted of stringing the offender to a gun or waggon wheel and leaving him exposed for long periods.
13 Blackader. 129–30.

INFANTRY

Although the cavalry still claimed precedence in the armies of the early eighteenth century, there were far more infantrymen on the battlefield. In general terms, an army of the period consisted of two-thirds infantry (the foot) and one-third cavalry (the horse), and thus the bulk of the men marched and fought on foot. As far as the tactical employment and the equipment of the troops were concerned, the period of the War of the Spanish Succession was one of radical change, hence its interest to students of military history.

Since the appearance of the first primitive hand-held firearms in the fifteenth century, the infantry arm of an army had been composed of varying ratios of pikemen to musketeers. The Swiss invented the mass phalanx of pikemen as an answer to feudal cavalry, and guns were originally used as an auxiliary weapon to support the pikes and disorganise the opposing force – after which the pikes would deliver the *coup de grâce*.

The lengthy loading process and chronic unreliability of the early matchlock muskets meant that infantry were powerless to resist cavalry once they had discharged their pieces. Thus the pikes had the additional function of protecting the musketeers, which guaranteed their retention as the numbers of those armed with guns increased throughout the sixteenth and seventeenth centuries. However, there was an additional sociological factor which ensured their survival. The pike was regarded as a far more respectable weapon than the noisy and odious gun, and to 'trail a pike' was considered in many countries to be a suitable occupation for a gentleman volunteer.

The pike itself was a cumbersome weapon, anything up to 18 feet long and weighing 17 and 20 pounds – although many soldiers tended to shorten their weapons by sawing off the bottom two or three feet. It consisted of a wooden shaft shod with a metal butt and with a pointed spear-like tip.

By the early part of the seventeenth century, the ratio was usually one-third pikes to two-thirds muskets, but as the century progressed, the pike was clearly on the way out – by the time of the 1688 revolution the ratio was nearer one to five. The basic reason for this was that the reliability and rate of fire of muskets had gradually improved – the faster a man could fire the less protection he required while loading. Generally speaking, by 1700 the pike had disappeared from European armies, although there were exceptions. The Swiss Guards in the French army retained their pikes up to 1703, and the Comte de Merode Westerloo, at the time in Spanish service, mentions their use by his troops at the Battle of Erckeren in 1703. Some regiments retained a small number of pikemen to guard the colours – hence the term picquet.

The other factor with regard to tactical changes that stemmed from the demise of the pike was that armies in battle formation could vastly extend their lines and thus the firepower that they could bring to bear. Instead of clumps

Fig. 10. A detail from the Wootton painting of the Battle of Blenheim showing infantry in combat at close quarters. Note the men loading muskets in the centre.

of pikemen mixed up between deep formations of musketeers, the latter became drawn up in long opposing lines of between three and five ranks deep.

However, the demise of the pike meant that infantry were still defenceless against cavalry unless an alternative could be found. This was provided for by the discovery of the bayonet, said to originate from the French town of Bayonne. The original ones were simply short daggers that plugged into the barrels of the muskets – converting the latter into a short pike. The snag was that when fixed, the troops could not fire, and the sight of their bayonets glinting in the light, advertised this fact to the enemy. General awareness of the faults of this *ad interim* solution led to the appearance of the socket bayonet which fitted over the barrel in-

stead of blocking it, and these were generally in use in most armies by 1703. Thus tactics were revolutionised by the invention of a short dagger.

At this stage we come to the chicken and egg problem when we attempt to discuss types of infantry, their equipment, organisation and tactical deployment. All have a bearing on each other, so it is best to start with the types of infantry to be found in European armies and to describe their weapons and equipment.

THE INFANTRY OF THE LINE

Such troops who formed the bulk of all eighteenth-century armies were basically equipped with a flintlock musket, a socket bayonet, a sword and a cartridge pouch. Such items were broadly speaking similar to all countries, and at the time, only hesitant steps towards standardisation were taking place. To list and discuss the muskets used by only the English army would require a volume to itself, and thus much of what follows is a generalisation.

THE MUSKET

The English word musket is normally used to refer to any form of smooth-bore muzzle-loading hand gun, and is derived from the French *mousquet* – which in turn refers to a distinct weapon, a musket fired by means of a matchlock. The situation is further complicated by the fact that the term used by many contemporary writers was *fusil* (corrupted in English as 'fusee'), which was the French name for a musket fired by a flintlock. Therefore it is preferable to classify the weapons of the period by the types of lock used to operate them.

The problem posed to the designer was to ignite the charge of powder rammed into the firing chamber at the base of the barrel, in order to produce an explosion of sufficient force to expel the ball over a satisfactory distance.

The earliest method of doing this was to apply the end of a length of glowing slow-match to a small amount of priming powder placed in a pan above the touch-hole. This was then refined into the actual match-lock whereby the match fixed to a cock was lowered into the pan by the action of pulling a trigger. This type of weapon was standard equipment throughout most of the seventeenth century.

A refinement came in the form of the wheel-lock in which a spring was tensioned by being wound up with a key. When released by the trigger action, this caused a serrated wheel to rub against a flint or pyrites – producing a stream of sparks similar to a modern cigarette lighter. Originally, the wheellock was popular for cavalry pistols as it meant that the weapon could be kept loaded and tensioned. However, when left tensioned for any length of time, they

tended to jam, and their complicated mechanism made them far too expensive for general issue to troops.

The matchlock was still in use to a certain extent in 1700, but it suffered from a number of major defects. The rate of misfire was chronic (in extreme cases every other round failed to go off), mainly caused by damp getting into the powder and poor handling. The loading time was far too long and an experienced man could seldom manage more than one round per minute. The 1690 drill exercises stipulated forty-four separate movements and the soldier was festooned rather like a Christmas tree with equipment. The charges were carried in twelve small wooden tubes slung from a bandolier around the shoulder (the Twelve Apostles). The soldier took one of the tubes, opened it and poured the contents into the muzzle of his musket. This was followed by a cloth wad, after which he had to open his pouch and take out a ball. After the whole issue had been well rammed down, he had to pour priming powder into the pan from his flask or horn, and then, with the weapon presented, he blew on his match to produce a good glow before being able to pull the trigger.

The glow of matches in the dark meant that troops were never able to hide themselves at night and the effects of bad weather could be catastrophic. The kick from these weapons was ferocious, and to avoid this, they were often fired with the butt tucked under the arm, much to the sacrifice of accuracy. Another reason for the lack of desire to shoulder all types of musket was the prevalence of flashbacks through the touch-hole, which did not do the eyebrows any good.

However, the type of musket with which we are concerned is the flintlock, often referred to by contemporaries in English as the firelock. This developed from the snaphaunce lock which produced a spark by releasing a hammer gripping a piece of flint and causing it to strike a steel plate. This type probably originated in Germany at the beginning of the seventeenth century, being initially used for

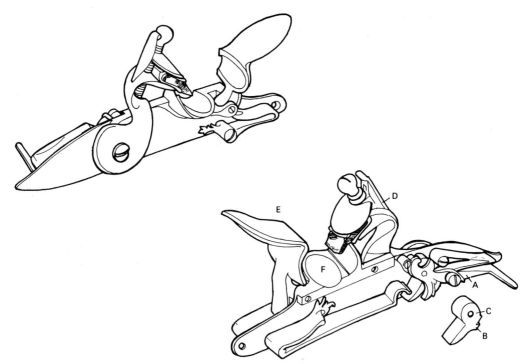

Fig. 11. Two views of a French flintlock. (A) sear; (B) half cock; (C) full cock; (D) cock or hammer; (E) frizzen or battery; (F) priming pan.

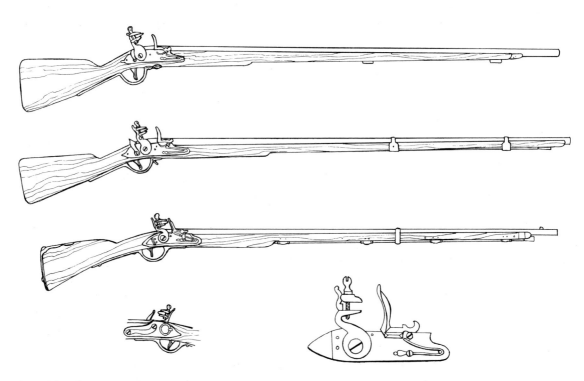

Fig. 12. Three British muskets – from top to bottom, 1704, 1722, 1715.

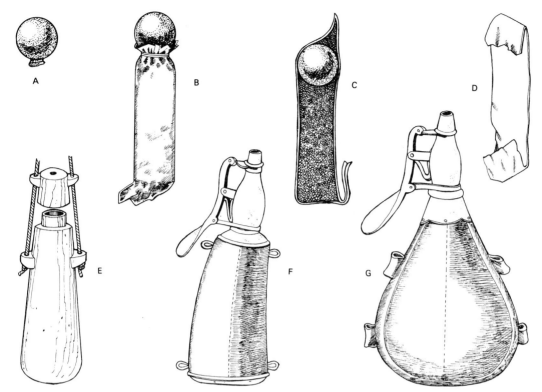

Fig. 13. (A) Ball showing rough piece left when removed from mould. (B) German musket cartridge with ball tied round the casting neck. (C) Section through paper cartridge enclosing ball. (D) Paper cartridge without ball. (E) Wooden cartridge. (F), (G) Priming flasks.

expensively crafted hunting weapons. From it developed the true flintlock in which the pan cover was an integral part of the steel striking surface.

Essentially, pulling the trigger caused the cock that held the flint to fly forward. As it struck the steel surface, the pan cover flew open and the sparks generated fell on to the priming powder.

Various forms of this basic weapon were in general use throughout Europe by 1700, although its introduction was a slow process. In addition to the inevitable resistance from conservatively minded officers, there was the question of expense. Colonels were unwilling to discard their older-type weapons until forced to, and governments were slow to offer them recompense. Snaphaunce muskets were first issued in England to the Lord High Admiral's regiment in 1665 for service on board ship –

where too many glowing matches in the vicinity of open powder barrels courted disaster, and because spray had a bad effect on the matches anyway. General re-equipment of the English and German infantry regiments took place during the late 1690s and in the more conservative French army by 1703. The Hapsburgs still had large numbers of matchlocks as late as 1710.

In range and accuracy the flintlock gained little over its immediate predecessors. However, it was lighter and thus more easily handled. In addition, flints proved more reliable than the damp-prone match which in turn reduced the rate of misfires. The introduction of paper cartridges had the effect of increasing the rate of fire.

Basically, the musket consisted of three parts – lock, stock and barrel, walnut being the wood preferred for the stock. Standardisation of muskets in the English service did not take place until 1716, when a pattern was laid down that was to grow into the 'Brown Bess', a weapon that was to remain in service until superseded during the 1830s.

Marlborough's troops used a variety of muskets of English manufacture when efforts were being made throughout Anne's reign to gear native production to the needs of a large army. These were supplemented by purchases from abroad, mostly from Holland, although many of the latter proved to be of inferior quality. Barrel lengths varied between 42 and 46 inches.[1]

The Brandenburg/Prussian army did have a standard pattern of musket issued shortly before 1700 during the reign of Frederick I – known as the *Kurbrandenburgische Grenadier-Flinte*, although it was not specifically for use by grenadiers. This had a total length of 1·95 metres with bayonet fixed and 1·53 without, and its total weight was 5·8 kilograms. The wooden ramrod was fitted into a slot under the barrel and held in place purely by friction. Ramrods came in various lengths and tapered gently almost to a point. The top end was a concave cup designed to fit around the ball.

The French had a fairly standard weapon known as the *fusil ordinaire* which, as we shall see later, had a considerably smaller calibre than similar English weapons – 0·68 inches compared with 0·85 inches.

The inherent disadvantages of the flintlock were many, all of which affected rate of fire and accuracy. A good flint withstood some thirty shots before being changed, and fifty was the absolute maximum. A really hard flint naturally lasted longer, but tended to wear out the striking surface – which then had to go to an armourer for a new piece to be riveted on. Soft flints splintered easily and could damage the users' eyes.

The greatest problem, however, was that of windage – the gap between the diameter of the ball and the diameter of the musket barrel. A tight fit was impossible as the use of black powder caused the interior of the barrel to become encrusted with deposits of half-burnt powder. After some thirty rounds the barrel had to be scraped out, as the fit of the ball became so tight that it was almost impossible to load. Furthermore, the recoil increased enormously and thus accuracy became impossible. The 'rolling fit' or amount of play between ball and the wall of the barrel was normally reckoned as between 0·04 and 0·07 inches. Another allied problem was that the touch-hole also became encrusted with powder remains and had to be cleared with a pricker.

Rate of fire was determined by the speed with which well-trained troops could load their weapons. For loading, four elements are required – charge, wadding, projectile and detonating medium. The term cartridge can only really be applied to an item that contains all of these, or at least three of them.

Two types of cartridge were developed for use with the flintlock musket. The earlier ones were simply a measured charge of powder wrapped in waxed paper – a direct successor to the wooden container on the bandolier. To load, the soldier bit off the end of the paper, poured in the powder and then stuffed the empty cartridge into the barrel to serve as a wad. He then took a bullet from his pouch and applied his ramrod (to speed loading, two bullets were often held in the mouth). After this had been done, he still had to prime his pan from a separate horn or flask, usually containing powder of a finer grain than the charge.

Cartridges of this type were issued to the Brandenburg infantry as early as 1670 when they began to re-equip with flintlocks. Instead of twelve bandolier charges, each man was given twenty-four cartridge rounds – a bandolier could be refilled from a bulk supply carried in a horn, but cartridges had to be made up separately. The method was to take a smooth stick of the required diameter, roll the paper around it, pour in the correct amount of powder and twist the ends.

However, to speed matters up even further, later cartridges included the bullet as an integral part. Normally it was simply enclosed in the paper casing, but a German authority shows a cartridge whereby the lead neck left on the bullet after casting was not removed. Instead, the paper was tied around this with a piece of thread. This latter type, however, was soon abandoned, as it had a negative effect on the ballistics of the weapon.[2]

As a final refinement, the use of a separate powder horn was abandoned and a small amount of the main charge was shaken from the cartridge into the pan. This was not very effective as the amount could not be accurately measured and the coarser grain of the charge powder was not really suitable for priming purposes. Again, accuracy was being sacrificed to rate of fire.

The following is the Prussian loading drill dated 1726, but basically the same as used towards the end of the War of the Spanish Succession:

'Each man must be taught how to quickly load and to use his weapon, and loading must be carried out as follows: when the weapon has been brought down to the right side the men must quickly de-cock the hammer and then rapidly grasp the cartridge. As soon as they have grasped the cartridge they must rapidly bite the same so that they taste powder in the mouth, then quickly shake the powder into a pan, the pan quickly close, throw the weapon sideways to load, but not spill the cartridge, upon which point great care must be taken. After this the cartridge must be introduced into the barrel and thoroughly emptied. The ramrod must be pulled out as rapidly as possible, rapidly turned around, the grip shortened, inserted into the barrel and be rammed down as hard as possible so that the charge is well compressed. Officers must observe and take care when a man does not push down his ramrod hard enough. After this the ramrod must be pulled out in one movement, the grip shortened, turned around and be replaced in its position.'[3]

Note the use of the word rapidly for virtually every movement! How much powder went into the pan and how much blew away was of no particular concern.

The business with the ramrod, however, needs some explanation. As the thin end of the long ramrod was inserted into the shaft below the barrel, it has to be turned around before the thick end could be inserted to ram down the charge. This movement had to be carried out with the arm extended in front so that the soldier did not obstruct his neighbour. After gripping the thick end, withdrawing it and turning it, the man's hand was too close to the ramming part to be able to insert it properly. Therefore the grip had to be 'shortened'. This was done by resting the ramrod against the body and allowing the right hand to slide upwards from the bottom to roughly the middle. Naturally, the reverse procedure applied after loading when the ramrod was withdrawn – the grip had again to be shortened before the rod could be turned and re-inserted into its holder.

The rate of fire under combat conditions in the early eighteenth century was said to be between two and three rounds per minute. However, in view of the extreme weight of the musket and general fatigue, this must be regarded as being only a short-term possibility. Besides in view of the above remarks concerning encrustation and wear of flints, after some thirty rounds most of the muskets of an infantry battalion would have been unserviceable. This ties in with the fact that the normal issue was twenty-four rounds of cartridge per man. As ammunition supply during a battle would hardly have been possible, it would seem that the average infantryman was not expected to fire more than the ammunition he could carry.

All these drills, however, were easily upset by the misfire problem which could never be entirely eradicated. Although the flintlock was a distinct improvement on the matchlock, the very lock mechanism had a built-in defect in the form of the two basic springs which it contained. If the frizzen spring was too weak, the impact of the cock (hammer) bent it forward and thus lowered resistance to the flint – result: too few sparks. If the hammer spring was too weak, it failed to open the pan cover fully. Ideally, the tensile strength of the two springs

25

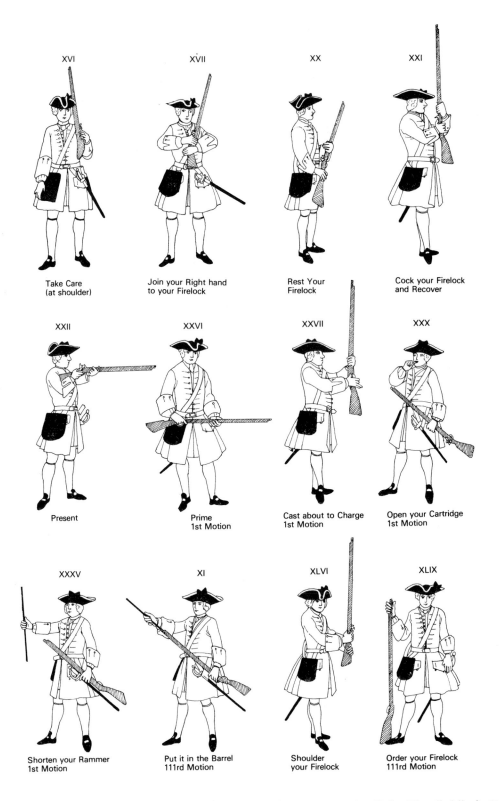

Fig. 14. The Manual Exercise. Simplified figures from Benjamin Gale, The Soldier's Pocket Companion, *1746. The figures relate to an earlier date, either 1728 or 1739.*

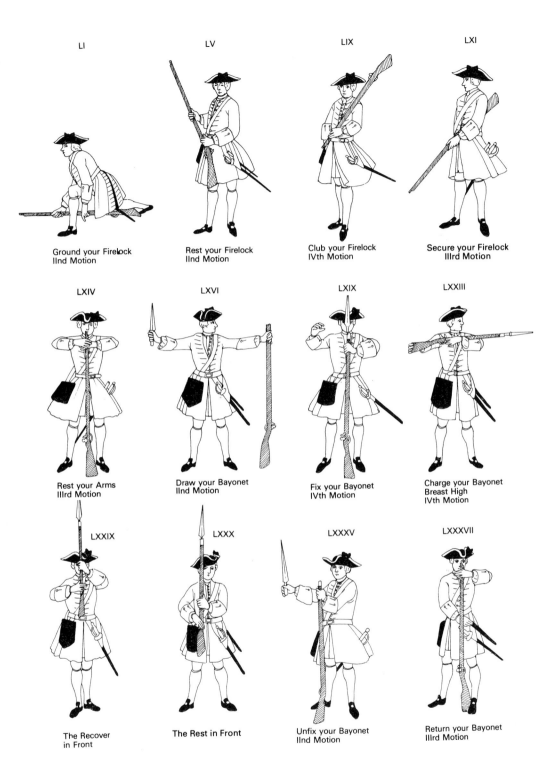

LI	LV	LIX	LXI
Ground your Firelock IInd Motion	Rest your Firelock IInd Motion	Club your Firelock IVth Motion	Secure your Firelock IIIrd Motion

LXIV	LXVI	LXIX	LXXIII
Rest your Arms IIIrd Motion	Draw your Bayonet IInd Motion	Fix your Bayonet IVth Motion	Charge your Bayonet Breast High IVth Motion

LXXIX	LXXX	LXXXV	LXXXVII
The Recover in Front	The Rest in Front	Unfix your Bayonet IInd Motion	Return your Bayonet IIIrd Motion

should have been matched to each other, but this was beyond the technology of mass-production at the time. In 1810, tests were carried out in Germany on muskets only slightly improved in general design, and under ideal range conditions resulted in 15 per cent. misfires – which could well have been trebled under combat conditions.

The noise of battle often caused troops to be unaware that their weapons had misfired, leading to double and triple charging as one round after another was rammed down the barrel. With such rigid emphasis on drill no soldier would draw attention to himself by fumbling about trying to unload his weapon to correct a misfire, and thus invite the ire of his superiors.

An interesting statistic that illustrates this problem comes from the American Civil War when, after Gettysburg, the North captured 27,000 muskets. 3,000 were found to be unloaded and 6,000 were correctly loaded, 12,000 were double charged and 6,000 were found to contain between three and ten charges rammed into the barrel – all at a time when the far more reliable percussion cap method of detonation was in general use.[4]

Everyone at the time realised that the musket was an extremely inaccurate weapon, but it was all that they had. Writing as late as 1757, Marshal de Saxe stated – 'the firearm is not so terrible as one thinks; few men are killed in action by fire from the front. I have seen volleys that did not hit four men. . . .'[5] This is probably somewhat of an exaggeration, as the casualties in the battles of the War of the Spanish Succession were comparatively high considering the numbers of men involved.[6]

Effective range of a flintlock musket was 200 to 300 paces, although the ball would travel some 1,000 paces when fired well elevated. Balls that hit the ground at around 250 paces could ricochet two or three times, thus extending their range somewhat. Aiming was not encouraged as it was a waste of time and interrupted the smooth flow of drill movements. In view of its extreme length, the barrel waved about in a wide arc and most weapons of the period were not fitted with any form of sighting marks.

However, the main reason for lack of accuracy was the inherent fault built into the weapon because of 'windage' – the gap between bullet and barrel wall. In any smooth-bore weapon, the ball lies on the bottom of the barrel rather than in the centre of the theoretical fore-and-aft axis. Furthermore, owing to inaccurate casting of the lead sphere, each ball has a different centre of gravity.

When the charge is fired, it does not hit the exact centre of the ball and thus imparts a twist to it as it starts to move off up the barrel – like a spin in billiards. This can be controlled by a good player but not by a musketeer – when each ball and quantity of powder in the charge are different. Further, during its travel along the barrel, the ball hits the wall several times, each time getting a different spin. When it leaves the muzzle it is influenced by the last of these wall impacts, which cannot, however, be calculated in advance.

The above fairly lengthy discussion on muskets in general is but a summary of various factors influencing their design and use. As is the case with any weapon, effectiveness could be measured in theoretical terms, but much depended upon the ability of the troops using them. The only real improvement made until rifles became generally adopted during the mid-nineteenth century was the introduction of the iron ramrod. This was issued to the Prussian army in 1718 under the auspices of Leopold of Anhalt-Dessau as a direct result of his experiences during the War of the Spanish Succession. Wooden ramrods broke easily and thus rendered a soldier unable to fire – he had to borrow his neighbour's which promptly upset the rhythm of drill. The iron ramrod, rapidly adopted by all European armies, vastly increased loading speed and thus killing capacity.

This latter factor is extremely difficult to calculate, given the inherent inefficiency of the musket. However, one guide is the actual weight of ball fired, which was often used as a method of weapon classification. The calibre of a hand weapon could be indicated by the weight of ball that it was designed to fire, described in terms of the number of balls to the pound 'rolling in' – i.e. a loose fit. A carbine (see section on cavalry weapons) firing ball of seventeen to the pound was spoken of as a 'seventeen bore'.

English and German muskets fired a much heavier ball than French models. Referring to relative firepower when discussing the Battle of Malplaquet, Captain Parker wrote – 'The advantage on our side will be easily accounted for, first from the weight of our ball; for the French arms carry bullets of 24 to the pound; whereas our British firelocks carry balls of only 16 to the pound, which will make a considerable difference to the execution.'[7]

THE BAYONET

The original plug bayonets appeared on the Continent around 1640 and were first issued to English troops of the Tangier garrison in 1663.[8] Their general issue, however, came after the 1688 revolution.

Plug bayonets consisted of a double-edged knife blade with a short varnished wooden haft and a brass ferrule to jam into the muzzle of the musket. This usually had a taper so that it would fit different weapons. Normally they were about one foot long overall, but in some cases the blade was lengthened to form a small sword. More expensive versions were made privately with silver-gilt decorations and finely wrought handles of ivory or horn.[9]

As already stated, the problem was that with the bayonet fixed, the troops could not fire. Another expedient tried in the search for a method whereby musketeers could defend themselves from cavalry was the use of short hunting spears that were planted into the ground in front of a line of infantry, pointing outwards towards the enemy. These were popular in Germany where they were known as *Schweinsfeder*, wrongly translated into English as 'Swedish feathers'.

The defects of the plug bayonet became sadly apparent at the Battle of Killiekrankie in 1689, when General Mackay's infantry with bayonets fixed were unable to fire and were routed by the Highlanders. According to Mackay's memoirs,[10] he invented a new type of bayonet as a result of this humiliation, which could be clamped under the barrel of a musket by means of two rings. (One is illustrated in Grose's *Military Antiquities*.)

Quite who invented the socket bayonet proper is not clear, although there is some evidence that the French engineer, Vauban, gave some attention to the matter in the 1670s. It appeared in Europe generally during the 1680s, finding grudging acceptance by colonels faced with the expense of re-equipping their regiments. The English and Germans had adopted it by around 1697, while the French waited until 1703.

Basically, it consisted of a metal blade, usually triangular in cross section, the base of which was drawn out and forged into a sleeve with a slit in one side. This was made to fit over a stud brazed on to the muzzle of the musket, and is the origin of the term 'bayonet fitting' still applied to British pattern light bulbs today. Once the socket was drawn over the muzzle, a quarter turn was required to lock it in place, resulting in a reasonably stable fitting. The early Prussian bayonets, however, relied on friction for their grip, until experience showed that the vibration of firing and the stream of gas from the muzzle caused them to fall off in action.

Another lesson learnt from practical experience was that a crank had to be induced into the neck between the blade and the socket. Otherwise, if the blade lay too close to the fore and aft line of the barrel, the soldier impaled his hand when wielding his ramrod.

Again, in English service, there is no real form of standardisation that can be traced. From correspondence between colonels of regiments and the Ordnance authorities, it would seem that the latter regarded it as the responsibility of the regiments to re-equip themselves at their own expense. A letter dated

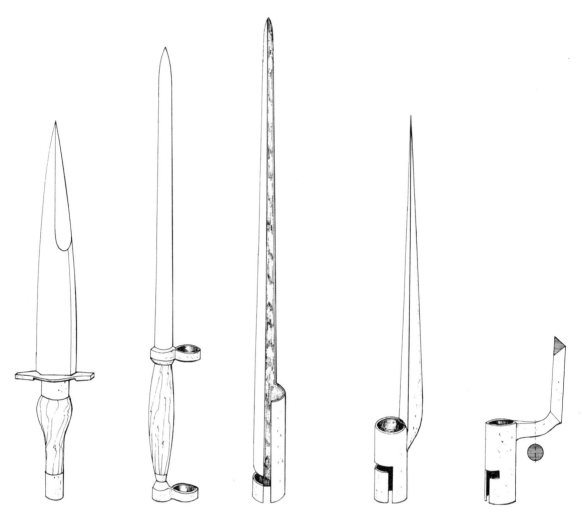

Fig. 15. Bayonets. Left to right, *plug bayonet, ring bayonet, early expanding socket bayonet, socket bayonet with blade drawn out straight and far right, with crank introduced.*

in 1706 started off by stating that bayonets could only be issued at public expense to grenadiers, and then went on – 'Few of the Officers agree on the sort of bayonets fit to be used or in the manner of fitting them to the Musquets [*sic*] as may appear by the various sorts that there are on them in ye Army.'[11]

As a rough guide, however, bayonets tended to be some 16 inches long and fit on the side of or underneath the barrel, while French ones were often fitted on top, thus disturbing the line of sight. One variant was the expanding socket bayonet of which there is an example in the Tower of London. In this, the slit runs the whole length of the socket, enabling it to be expanded to fit various diameters of musket barrel. In view of the differences in muskets used, this type must have been popular with colonels.

The odd factor is that during the period of the War of the Spanish Succession, the tactical use of the bayonet was largely passive. In the Brandenburg/Prussian army, for example, the bayonet was never fixed when firing was taking place. It was carried in action from a leather sling worn over the shoulder and only fitted when a cavalry attack threatened. The probable reason for this was that the musket was a clumsy weapon for use in a thrusting role, and

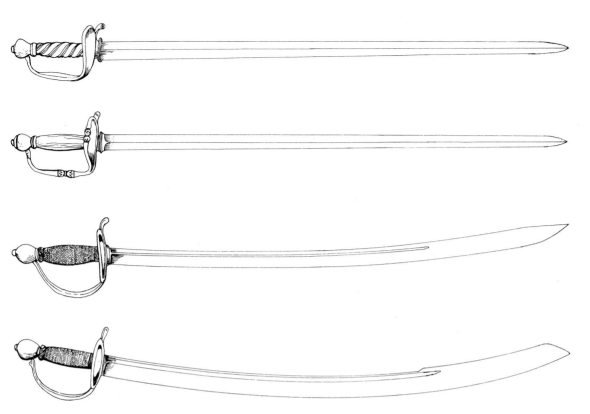

Fig. 16. Examples of French infantry swords, circa 1700. Top, *two fusilier pattern swords.* Bottom, *two grenadier hangers.*

in a storm attack the troops may well have preferred to throw away their firearms and get to grips with their swords. To receive cavalry, the front rank of an infantry unit would kneel and plant the butts of their muskets in the ground, slanting the bayonets outwards − leaving the rear ranks to fire at the advancing horse.

In addition to the Prussian method mentioned above, bayonets were carried in various ways. Sheathed in leather scabbards, they could be worn from the sword belt on the left side or above the sword itself on a double frog. St Rémy shows an illustration of a French system whereby the bayonet was clipped above the cross strap of the cartridge pouch.

INFANTRY SWORDS

In all armies of the period, the infantry were issued with swords worn generally on the left hip, slung from the belt in a leather frog. The leather scabbard had a hook at the top which fitted into a slot in the frog, thus holding it in place and enabling the sword to be drawn. This was, however, a two-handed operation − one hand to hold the scabbard rigid and the other to pull out the blade. Therefore, the musket had first to be disposed of somehow.

In view of the vast numbers of swords used, one cannot be really specific. However, the most popular type was the short sword or hanger, fitted into a leather scabbard with brass or steel fittings. Blades were usually double edged and tapering to a fairly sharp point. The guard was formed out of two lobes of solid metal which were taken back in the form of a thick bar over the grip and jointed to the pommel. The grip itself was often wound with silver wire, covered with leather or otherwise roughened. It ended in a heavy round pommel, commonly marked with a regimental or royal emblem.

31

Fig. 17. Staff weapons. The two on the left are a French spontoon and halberd. Note Sun King emblem. On the right are a Prussian spontoon and halberd with monogram of King Frederick William I.

STAFF WEAPONS

Regiments naturally tended to buy the cheapest available and there was little apparent standardisation. In many ways, the infantry sword was of more use as a tool than as a weapon. Its practical uses were for gathering firewood, hacking down brushwood for making fascines, reaping corn and for intimidating reluctant peasantry and innkeepers.

Officers' swords were longer and more ornate, similar to those worn as an adjunct to dress in civilian life. Their main practical use was for duelling, as in battle the lower commissioned ranks were armed with spontoons while the higher ranks could only have resorted to their swords when really hard pressed by the enemy.

As direct ancestors of the pike and perhaps even the mediaeval lance as a symbol of authority, officers and nco's of the various European armies continued to carry staff weapons until the middle of the nineteenth century in some cases. These had little practical use for fighting and were purely marks or indications of rank.

Subalterns and captains carried a spear-like weapon known as a spontoon (*Sponton* in German and *esponton* in French). This had developed from the partizan, and was in effect, a short pike. It had a wooden shaft, between seven and nine feet long, and a steel or brass tip, usually engraved with a royal or regimental cipher. In practical terms, these weapons were fairly visible on a smoke-filled battlefield and

Fig. 18. The Wynandael tapestry showing a sergeant of the Royal Scots threatening a carter with his halberd. De Vos after L. de Hondt.

could thus act as a rallying point. Officers tended to use them for dressing ranks and for forcing down musket barrels that were pointing too high. Would-be deserters could also be prodded back into the ranks.

Sergeants in infantry companies were equipped with halberds, again a mediaeval throwback. These also had shafts some nine feet long and one side of the point formed an axe blade – often decorated with complicated engraving.

PERSONAL EQUIPMENT

Apart from his basic uniform clothing that will be dealt with in a later chapter, the infantry soldier required various items of equipment in

33

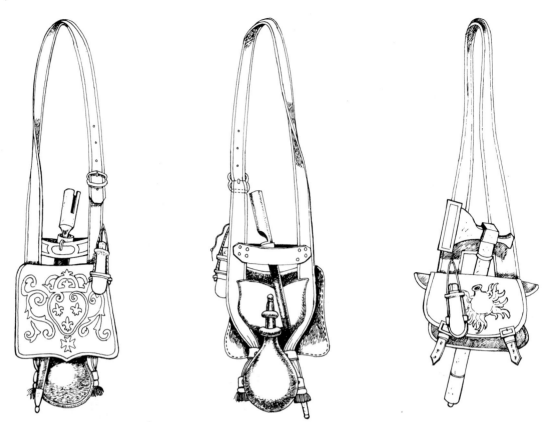

Fig. 19. Infantry equipment, including socket bayonet, after St Rémy. Left, front and rear views of infantry equipment showing water bottle slung behind pouch. On the right, grenadier equipment with hatchet.

order to be able to function in combat and use his weapons. This naturally varied from regiment to regiment and from country to country – as is soon apparent to the researcher who endeavours to make sense of the mass of contemporary illustrations.

Body armour as such disappeared during the same period as the demise of the pike, although the Swiss Guards in French service clung to theirs until well into the eighteenth century. The only vestige to remain was the gorget worn as a badge of rank in many armies by infantry officers. This was a metal half-moon shape worn around the neck suspended by a cord or metal chain, although often obscured by the neckcloth in paintings. In England, a Royal Warrant dated 1684 'for the better distinction of our several officers serving us in our Companies of Foot', laid down that captains should wear gold coloured ones, lieutenants ones of black studded with silver while those for ensigns were to be of polished silver or steel.

Certainly the officers of most French regiments wore them, and during the period covered by the War of the Spanish Succession, they were coming into use in the Prussian and other German armies. They were normally finely engraved with royal arms or regimental symbols, although the French ones were apparently plain.[12]

Otherwise, officers carried nothing on their person by way of equipment except for their swords. Some tapestries show officers wearing their swords slung from fabric baldrics worn loosely over the shoulder. In others, the sword

34

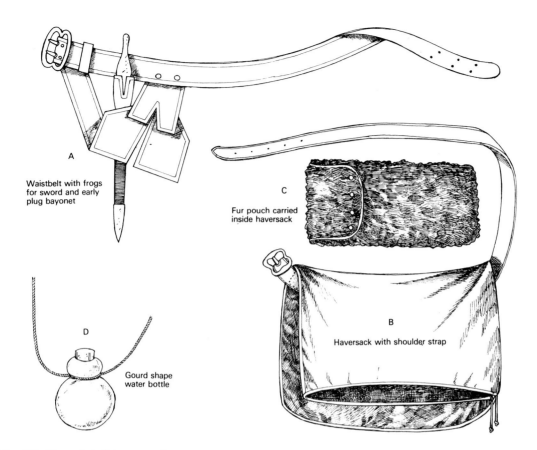

A
Waistbelt with frogs
for sword and early
plug bayonet

C
Fur pouch carried
inside haversack

D
Gourd shape
water bottle

B
Haversack with shoulder strap

Fig. 20. French infantry equipment.

peeps out from under their full skirts, leading one to assume that they were fixed to a frog hanging from a belt.

The equipment of the ordinary soldiers can be brought down to certain essential items that were common to most armies. All wore a broad belt fastened by a buckle at the front. This carried the sword and, in some cases, the bayonet. Some illustrations show the cartridge box or pouch worn on the belt to the right of the buckle.

Cartridge pouches, however, were generally slung from a broad strap worn over the left shoulder and running down to the right hip. Such straps were made of buff leather or were pipe-clayed white. The pouches were either of buff leather or black leather and closed by a flap which displayed some sort of emblem. In the Prussian army this was the monogram F.R. for *Fredericus Rex*.

It is difficult to determine the exact contents. The French carried twenty cartridges and the Prussians and English were issued with twenty-four. The latter also carried some spare flints. The Prussian infantry carried three spare flints, a stopper to close off the muzzle of their musket in wet weather, a scraper, a needle for clearing the touch-hole, an oil bottle and a rag and brush for cleaning purposes.

When a separate priming medium was used, this was carried in a small horn or flask likewise suspended over the left shoulder from a strap. This was probably worn fairly long as it had to be able to be grasped and brought to the pan of the musket without being detached from the strap.

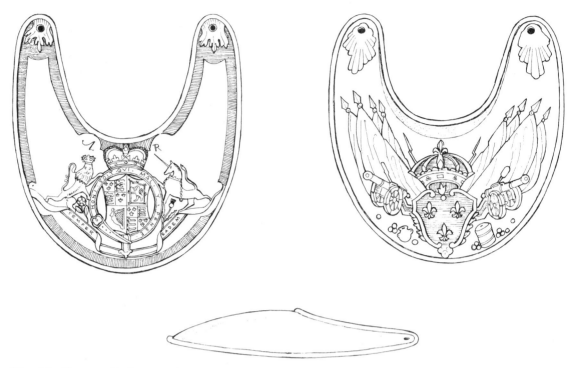

Fig. 21. Gorgets. Left, *British pattern Queen Anne period.* Right, *French gorget with Royal arms.* Below, *cross-section.*

It would seem that water-bottles (probably often containing stronger liquids) were carried, but I have been unable to discover any solid information about them. They do not feature on English equipment lists and the only good illustration I have found is in St Rémy. He shows a flat round container which was carried underneath the cartridge pouch. The Prussian march order given below mentions them but gives no description.

For his personal possessions (and loot) the early eighteenth-century soldier had a haversack which was simply a cloth bag worn on the back and attached to a strap passing over the shoulder. As the men were sometimes expected to carry sufficient bread for up to four days, the Prussians had an additional bread-bag as a separate item of kit. In addition, a soldier might have to carry a cooking-pot, and Kane mentions that before going into battle a good officer ordered his men 'to lay down their knapsacks, tent-poles and what is cumbersome'. From this, one can assume that they were expected to carry tent-poles, although I prefer to think that such items were normally borne on the company waggons, along with entrenching tools. In the French army, a number of men in each company carried spades, for which they received extra pay.

Musket slings were normally only issued to grenadiers and fusiliers, and the line infantry shouldered their weapons while marching. It has been estimated that an English soldier had to carry some 50 pounds of equipment, including his musket, and the Prussian march order was as follows:

Cartridge Pouch
Haversack
Bread-bag
Bottle
Kettle
Musket
Sword
Spade (under certain circumstances)
Total weight – circa 65 pounds.

Fig. 22. Detail of a grenadier from the Blenheim tapestry. Note the field dressing station in background left. The grenadier is guarding captured trophies.

GRENADIERS

As the name implies, this type of infantry soldier was used for the throwing of hand grenades or *grenadoes* as they were sometimes called in contemporary literature. When, during the course of the eighteenth century, grenades went out of fashion, the name was retained for élite units. The present Grenadier Guards were the 1st Foot in Marlborough's time and only gained their present title for their performance at Waterloo – when they did not use grenades!

The *Military Dictionary* published in 1702 described them as follows:

'Grenadoes are small shells, concave Globes or hollow balls, some made of Iron, some of Tin, others of wood, and even of Pasteboard; but most commonly of iron, because the splinters of it do most Execution. This globe or Hollow is fill'd with Fine Powder, and into the touch-hole of it is stuck a Fuze full of powder, beaten and tempered with charcoal dust, that it may not flash, but burn gently till it comes to the Charge.'

In addition to the materials listed above, I have seen glass grenades in German museums. Generally their size was about that of a cricket ball, and the name is said to originate from the Spanish word *grenada* or pomegranate.

Grenadiers as a separate entity made their appearance in European armies in the mid

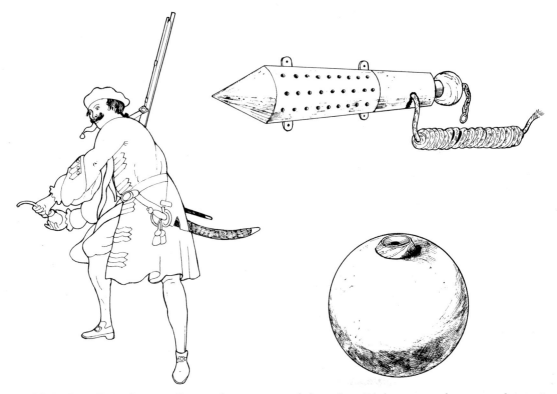

Fig. 23. Left, *a French grenadier at the moment of throwing*. Right, *a match case and a typical grenade*.

seventeenth century, at first in small numbers. They were selected from among the tallest men from the various infantry companies of a battalion – for the simple reason that they could be expected to throw their bombs the farthest. In France in 1667, four men per company were picked as grenadiers, but by 1670, the practice of forming a separate grenadier company for each battalion was accepted. As élite troops, they took the place of honour on the right of the line.

Such company establishments were first made in England in 1678, which was noted by John Evelyn the diarist. 'Now were brought into service a new sort of soldiers called Grenadiers, who were dextrous to fling hand grenades, each one having a pouch full, and had furr'd caps with coped crowns like Janizzaries, which made them look very fierce.'[13]

The reference to the headgear is interesting, as in course of time, this developed into the distinguishing mark of the grenadier units in all armies. Like most items of military display which may appear ridiculous, there was originally a valid reason for the adoption of different hats. In Mallet's book *Les Traveaux de Mars* originally published in 1673, there is a fine illustration of a grenadier wearing a floppy plumed hat. However, as the men had to have their arms free for throwing or bowling their grenades, their slung muskets tended to knock off the usual type of hat. These were replaced at first by a simple stocking cap trimmed with fur, the point of which hung loose, but by around 1700, these had been modified into the mitre pattern that was to remain the fashion throughout the century. To stiffen the cap into a point, a cloth-covered plate was added to the front and richly embroidered – English ones often bore the royal coat of arms and Anne's motto *Semper Eadam* – forever the same. Later, the front plates tended to be made of brass and highly polished.

Being recruited from the tallest men, the

Fig. 24. Engraving by Guerard of grenadiers. The man is just about to apply his match to the fuze. The other figure is a horse grenadier.

Fig. 25. Grenadiers attacking the covered-way of a fortress. Engraving from St. Rémy.

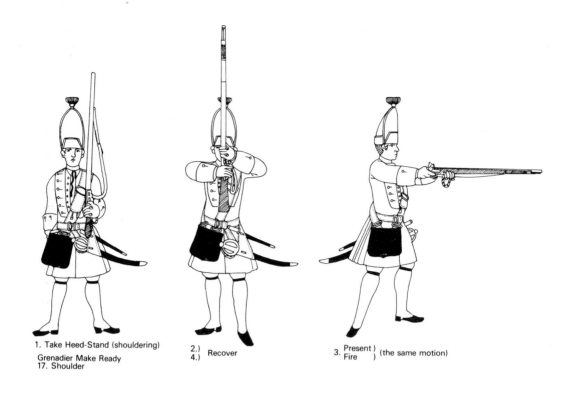

1. Take Heed-Stand (shouldering)

Grenadier Make Ready
17. Shoulder

2.)
4.) Recover

3. Present)
   Fire   ) (the same motion)

5. Handle Your Slings

6. Handle Your Slings
   (Second motion)

7. Sling Your Firelock

8. Handle Your Match

Fig. 26. 'The Grenadiers Exercise of the Grenade'. Based on a contemporary drawing.

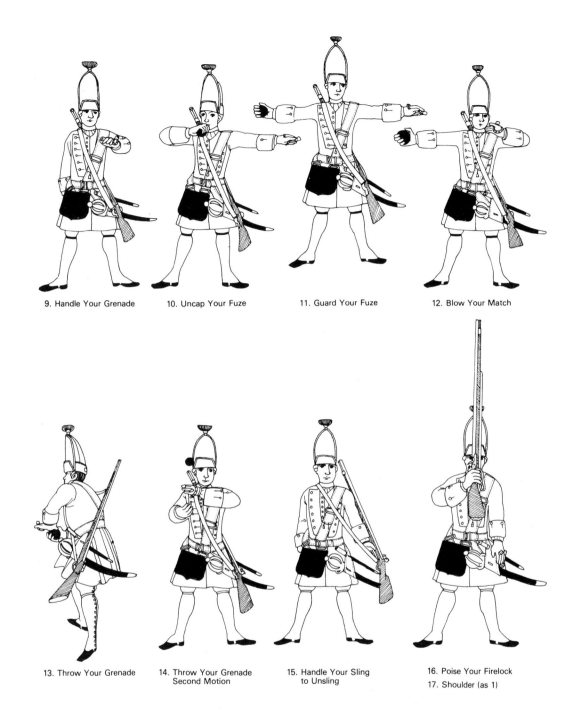

9. Handle Your Grenade

10. Uncap Your Fuze

11. Guard Your Fuze

12. Blow Your Match

13. Throw Your Grenade

14. Throw Your Grenade
Second Motion

15. Handle Your Sling
to Unsling

16. Poise Your Firelock

17. Shoulder (as 1)

grenadier companies soon assumed the role of shock troops used for storming parties or being formed up at the point of greatest danger on the battlefield. At times, the separate grenadier companies were brought together to form a larger composite unit.

Sergeant Kite addressed some prospects thus:

'. . . I don't beat up for common soldiers. No, I list only grenadiers, grenadiers, gentlemen. Pray, gentlemen, observe this cap. This is the cap of honour; it dubs a man a gentlemen in the pulling of a tricker [sic]; and he that has the good fortune to be born six foot high was born to be a great man.'

Fig. 27. Blenheim, by Laguerre. On the left, grenadiers are shown crossing the Nebel stream urged on by a sergeant with a halberd. On the right is Marlborough.

It is clear from the above and from such contemporary tunes as the Grenadier March and the British Grenadiers (see later section on military music) that the prestige of a grenadier was popularly accepted.

Apart from his ability to throw bombs, a grenadier needed to be tall on account of the extra equipment that he was expected to carry. Like the line infantryman, he had a musket, bayonet and sword to enable him to fight as part of his battalion. His grenades were carried in a pouch, larger than the normal cartridge one, worn on the right hip and hanging free from a very broad leather strap over the left shoulder.

These pouches had an emblem on the flap, and at this time the flaming grenade motive was already making its appearance – which still features on the regimental badges of a number of British units today. English grenadiers carried only three grenades in their pouches, but the French had between twelve and fifteen stored in their *grenadières*.

De la Colonie listed the equipment carried by his men as follows – 'over and above the clothes they stood in, their equipment was composed of gun, bayonet, heavy sword, grenade pouch, a pistol in their shoulder belt and a hatchet'.[14]

Pistols were not issued to the English grenadiers, and by 1700 hatchets were going out of fashion. However, they continued to be issued in the French army, worn either in a loop on the back of the waist belt or tucked in behind the pouch. The purpose of these was for hacking down wooden palisades when attacking fortifications.

Grenades could either be thrown in volleys as a drill movement, or individually when a target presented itself. Their use was restricted to storm attacks on fortifications, for if thrown in battle they would have caused equal damage to both friend and foe. To make a throw, the grenadier slung his musket, took a grenade from his pouch, bit or broke off the wax seal protecting the fuze and lit it from a piece of slow match that he kept coiled around his left wrist. He then did his best to get rid of his bomb as swiftly as possible.

When not in use, a length of match was carried in a match case and ready lit. The case was a brass tube some 9 inches long, with a wooden or brass stopper, and perforated with holes to allow air to circulate to keep the match glowing.

Fig. 28. Malplaquet by Laguerre. In the foreground, two grenadiers are helping to remove a felled tree. Note the dead who have already been stripped.

This was worn high on the shoulder belt, and the stopper was attached to a button by a short length of chain to avoid it getting lost. Some illustrations of grenadiers show them with a touch-hole pricker and a small pan-cleaning brush hanging from the tongue of the shoulder belt, just below the buckle.

As if to mark their separate identity, officers of grenadier companies carried muskets instead of the purely decorative spontoons, and in place of the ensign there was an extra lieutenant.

FUSILIERS

This type of infantryman appeared in the French army in 1671 when a regiment was raised specifically to guard the artillery train. Their name comes from the French *fusil* or flintlock musket with which they were armed and thus to differentiate between them and the normal line infantry still largely armed with matchlocks.

The reason for their use of the flintlock was that matches in the vicinity of open powder barrels were an invitation to danger. They were given muskets which were slightly lighter than the standard pattern and issued with slings. This was to enable them to keep their hands free for manhandling the cumbersome guns if required. A further distinguishing feature was their headdress – a conical fur cap similar to but not as tall as a grenadier cap.

The first fusiliers in England were the North British, raised by Charles II in 1678, and under James II two further regiments were added in 1685 and 1688 – the Royal Fusiliers and the Royal Welch Fusiliers.

However, their special status as guards of the artillery train did not last for long. As more and more regiments were re-armed with flintlocks, their originality ceased, and by 1700 the English fusilier regiments had become absorbed into the line infantry, although they retained their titles. During the War of the Spanish Succession, normal regiments were simply detached for service with the Train as and when required. The same tendency happened in France, but there the fusiliers were eventually absorbed into the artillery rather than the infantry.

Finally, it should be mentioned that guards for the Train were not only required to protect the guns and stores from surprise attack by the enemy – they were also there to stop the civilian drivers from running away!

INFANTRY ORGANISATION

In reading about the eighteenth-century armies, confusion is often caused by the terms regiment and battalion, although in the English army the two were usually synonymous. The battalion was essentially a tactical formation, but most English regiments had only one, the exceptions being the Guards. On the Continent, multi-battalion regiments were more common. A regiment was an administrative entity, owned by its colonel, with a headquarters staff.

The English army of the period consisted of the 'subject troops' raised in the British Isles. They were organised in regiments whose seniority was determined by the date they were first raised. Apart from specialist or royal units, they were known by the name of their colonel, but after 1712 they were numbered according to seniority which determined their position in the line.

The foreign contingents, who were paid by the government, tended to be organised along English lines, although officered by their own nationals.

On the Continent, there were vast differences in numbers and organisational methods, although the basics remained the same. The Empire, for example, fielded armies made up from the regiments of the Hapsburg territories, contingents provided by the various princes, and various auxiliaries mainly hired from the eastern frontiers.

In the French army, the household troops (the *Maison du Roi*) formed the right of the line, and were followed in seniority by a number of 'old' regiments, many of which were named after provinces or geographic areas. They were followed by foreign mercenaries who also formed a part of the regular army – the Irish 'Wild Geese' and the Swiss. The rest of the army was made up of regiments raised for the duration of a particular war and disbanded afterwards.

It is very difficult to be precise about relative strengths as the established figures seldom equalled the actual numbers of men present. Many regiments had a smaller peacetime establishment which was filled out on mobilisation. As a rough guide, an English battalion mustered around 800 officers and men, but 500 could well be the actual figure for those present at any one time. French battalions were slightly smaller – between 600 and 700 of all ranks, averaging two per regiment. Prussian regiments were also sub-divided into two battalions, while the Austrians had much larger ones split into four.

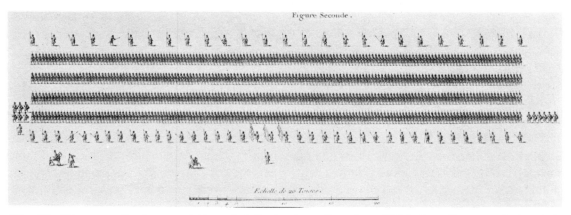

Fig. 29. Diagram of a four rank French infantry battalion circa 1706, from Puysegur's Art de la Guerre. *Note the position of the officers and nco's, and the drummers.*

The various *corps d'élite* – royal body-guards and household troops – represent a host of anomalies which are beyond the scope of this book.[15] However, certain basic elements can be determined. Firstly, officers and men in élite formations generally received more pay than their counterparts in line regiments, and their commanders were often very prominent personalities. The various French regiments were usually reserved for the King himself or Princes of the Blood, under whom it was an honour to serve as a company commander. Marlborough himself commanded the 1st Foot Guards until his disgrace in 1712, and again in 1714 when he was restored to favour.

Another factor was that such units generally had a larger establishment in terms of numbers – they represented the prestige of the monarch they served and were expected to make a fine showing on parade and in combat. Besides, the extra rates of pay helped to attract the better kind of recruit.

Turning now to the lower echelons, we have already seen that in Marlborough's day the brigade was a tactical formation formed by the banding together of two or more regiments. The most important formation for administrative purposes was the regiment, upon which all armies based their organisation. This was either the property of the Crown, or as in most countries, owned by its colonel – who had either raised it from scratch, bought it from someone else or had been presented with it by a grateful sovereign.

In the English army, a regiment was in theory commanded by its colonel, but as the latter could well be a general, command of the single battalion in the field would devolve on the lieutenant-colonel. The third senior man was the major, and in the case of a two-battalion regiment, there would be a major for each.

Regimental headquarters consisted of the quartermaster, the adjutant, chaplain, surgeon and his mate, solicitor, drum-major and the deputy marshal.[16] The solicitor and deputy marshal only applied in Guards regiments. A quartermaster was responsible for the business of his unit, keeping accounts of receipts and seeing to the issue of stores, food, tools, etc. A contemporary account stated that 'a Quarter-master of a Regiment ought to be an honest careful man'.[17] The same source enjoined an adjutant to 'choose three or four good sergeants that can write well' to wait on the officers as orderlies and messengers. Like his modern counterpart, the adjutant's job was to keep lists of duties, guards, men going sick, etc.

The above scheme could generally apply to any army of the period subject to local variations. In the same way, the battalions of a regiment were split into a number of companies – which were both tactical and administrative in that they were the property of the captain commanding. Indeed, the colonel, lieutenant-colonel and even the major of a regiment could own companies, in order to pocket the pay and profits, leaving them to be commanded in battle by a senior lieutenant.

An English battalion was divided into thirteen companies, one of grenadiers and twelve of musketeers. The number of privates varied from the established sixty per company, down to thirty or forty. The issue was further complicated by the problem of 'widows' men' and officers' servants, already alluded to. The French had a similar thirteen company subdivision, each established at fifty nco's and men. The German armies tended to have far larger companies. In Prussian service, the battalions of a two-battalion regiment were split into one grenadier and five musket companies, each with some 120 men. The large Austrian regiments with a strength of 2,300 (nominal) were divided into one grenadier and sixteen musket companies, which for tactical purposes became four battalions. Thus each of the latter had four companies each of some 150 men and a detachment of grenadiers.

The English infantry company normally had three officers – captain, lieutenant and ensign (second lieutenant in the case of grenadier companies). A typical establishment of nco's was thus three sergeants, three corporals and two drummers (paid as corporals).

TACTICAL EMPLOYMENT

The tactics employed at any period are largely determined by the weapons available, and in a previous section we have seen the limitations and disadvantges of the flintlock musket. This book deals with weapons and equipment and is not a general history of early eighteenth-century warfare. Therefore the following comments refer to tactics in so far as they were affected by the weaponry available and are not a general discussion on the tactics of individual battles.

As the bulk of armies were composed of infantry armed with flintlock muskets, the object of the exercise was to draw up the troops in two opposing lines and to produce as great a volume of fire as possible. The greater rate of fire of the flintlock meant that fewer ranks needed to be formed than was the case with the matchlock — owing to its slow-loading process six ranks were required and men had to file to the rear to reload. Another advantage of the more modern weapon was that troops needed less lateral room to operate it, thus the ranks could be placed closer together to deliver more fire for a given length of front.

At all times, shooting to produce a dispersed pattern of fire has required some form of machine. However, as the flintlock was not a machine, it followed that the troops themselves had to fulfil this function, being drilled to the extent that they became firing automata.

Methods of drill and the manner in which the troops were drawn up to produce that fire, however, tended to vary from country to country and even from regiment to regiment. It was not until slightly later in the century that the different armies began to lay down 'official' methods enshrined in drill books. The various textbooks available are interesting, but do not prove that a particular system was generally used at any one time. From the English point of view, the book by Brigadier-General Kane who served under Marlborough in the Royal Regiment of Foot of Ireland is the most valuable.

Common to all armies were certain basic essentials that any soldier had to master. Firstly there were the 'postures' – the movements concerned with weapon handling, saluting, etc. The numbers of individual movements differed, but a French order issued in 1703 specified sixty-seven. A man had to be able to slope arms, order arms, fix and unfix bayonets, go through the loading process and master the firing drill — both by spoken word of command and drum tap. In addition to these individual exercises, the soldiers then had to learn to move together under their officers. The column of march of six files had to be transformed to the three or four rank line and the companies had to be able to wheel to right or left and countermarch. Once in line, they had to open or close the distance between ranks, advance and retire, and form defensive squares.

The essence of linear tactics was firm discipline — once the line became disordered it was an open invitation to cavalry attack. Therefore the men had to be firm under fire, no matter how damaging, and as their comrades fell, they had to close the gaps in the ranks — there was no taking cover behind a convenient rock or bush.

This all may seem odd to our eyes, but as I said, tactics are determined by the limitations of weapons. As the individually aimed shot was so hopelessly unreliable and could not be improved upon by any known form of musket, the only way to achieve results was to have as many soldiers as possible firing at the enemy to give a spread or 'machine-gun' effect. Indeed, they went as far as to deliberately discourage the use of individually aimed shots if thereby the rate of fire of the mass could be improved.

In addition to the inherent inaccuracy of the musket itself, which has been discussed in a previous section, there were other human factors which played a part in influencing its effectiveness. The ferocious kick tended to drive the muzzle upwards at the moment of firing, and drill methods accentuated this problem. In the effort to get as many men into the front as possible, the tendency was to squash them together. With the front rank of a three-rank line kneeling, the third rank had to fire between the shoulders of the second, but found it difficult to get their weapons up to the aiming position, and preferred to fire over the heads of the men in front. Another factor was the actual weapon drill itself and the emphasis on speed at all costs. When a platoon fired a salvo, each man pressed the trigger and immediately, without further command, lowered the weapon in order to load. In the heat of battle, it is reasonable to assume that the muzzle was already moving upwards and the butt downwards before the ball was on its way.

This tendency to fire high was recognised, and officers had to use their spontoons to knock down barrels that were pointing skywards. The aiming point was given as the 'middle man' of the enemy, i.e. his waist, but many officers ordered their men to aim at the enemies' shoe buckles.

The above general considerations applied to all armies, but their methods of delivering fire differed. Let us look first at the system employed by the Dutch, English and some of the German armies, who in many respects were in advance of the more conservative French. The following is largely based on Kane's *Discipline for a Regiment of Foot*.

Assuming that the army was in contact with the enemy, the column of battalions marched on to the battlefield and moved off to left and right in a pre-determined order to form a line – reducing themselves in the process from six to three ranks. All this took an inordinate amount of time, and there was still a chance for the enemy to slip away and refuse to engage if he so desired.

The battalion formed its line in a predetermined order of companies with the colonels and lieutenant-colonels in the centre with the colours, while the grenadier company split to form a detachment at each end. A battalion was normally accompanied by two small 3-pounder field guns which were also drawn up on each flank.

This use of light manoeuvrable artillery was not invented by Marlborough as has been claimed, but he made great use of these 'battalion pieces' in battle – loaded with grape shot referred to at the time as 'partridge'. Their job was to demoralise the enemy before the infantry came into firing range.

At this stage the two opposing armies would be facing each other, still in some confusion, about 250 yards apart. According to Kane, 'when the commanding officer finds there is no avoiding coming to battle' he is to order any baggage to be 'sent to some place out of the way. . . . If we win the day they will be safe; if not, 'tis no matter what becomes of them.'

The battalion was then split into four 'Grand Divisions' each of three companies (excluding the grenadiers) and each of these into four platoons, from the French word *peleton*. In this way the thirteen company battalion became a fighting unit of eighteen platoons – sixteen from the Grand Divisions plus the two grenadier detachments. Thus, in combat, the company ceased to have any significance.

It is this split into platoons that provides the key to the most effective method then devised of fire delivery. Previously the normal way was for a battalion to fire by ranks or by divisions, under the assumption that one-third of the unit would be ready to fire at any one time while the rest were reloading. In practice, however, fire control was difficult with such large groups and it was difficult to maintain an unbroken rhythm of firing.

It is probable that the idea originated in Holland, but by 1700 it had certainly been adopted in England, and was used by the Brandenburg/Prussian army during the War of the Spanish Succession. Each platoon was divided into three 'firings' by the senior officers in a dispersed pattern along the line and the whole battalion loaded and primed their weapons. In overall command was the senior officer (colonel or lieutenant-colonel) who stood at the front with his drummer, while the rest of the drums marched to the rear. The company officers spread themselves in the intervals between the platoons to supervise firing or likewise formed up at the rear – to hinder any temptation to run away.

The battalion was then ready to advance into

action, and when the general command was given, the whole line advanced to some 60 paces from the enemy, marching to the tap of the drums while the artillery kept up an incessant bombardment. As men fell, the ranks closed up to fill the gaps.

Having marched into range, the colonel ordered 'halt' and then told the drummer 'to beat a preparative, upon which the six platoons of the first firing make ready . . . and the front rank kneels placing their butts on the ground by their left feet, where all are to wait for the next word of command or signal of the drum from the Colonel himself . . . and if he finds his voice not sufficient, he then orders his drummer to beat a "flam"; at which time the front rank, drop their muzzles to the ground and the rear two ranks present. . . . The Colonel orders the drummer to beat a second "flam", on which they fire and immediately recover their arms, fall back and load as fast as they can.'

The above extract from Kane describes the motions and demonstrates the fact that the fire of the front rank was often held back as a reserve. Once a 'firing' had discharged its pieces, the men stepped back into 'open order', loaded and closed up again ready to fire. In this position the ranks were only one foot apart – each man stood with his left shoulder and left foot forward presenting himself diagonally to the enemy, thus enabling the rear rank to fire between the men in front.

In some units, the platoons of each 'firing' fired by numbers to produce a rippling effect up and down the line, but this required tremendous discipline and control. Amid the din of battle and the clouds of black smoke, the platoon officers had to count in order to be able to tell when it was their turn to fire. Most commanding officers preferred all the platoons of each 'firing' to discharge their muskets together as a result of a single order.

The Prussian system was slightly different. A battalion in line divided into four companies each with two platoons – the resulting order of fire was 1, 3, 5, 7, 2, 4, 6, 8, to provide the difficult ripple effect, and it was a matter of

honour for the officers to ensure that their platoon did not disturb the rhythm.

Assuming that all the men were standing with loaded and shouldered muskets, the command *fertig* (make ready) was given. All then lifted their muskets vertically in front of their faces with the lock roughly at mouth level. The front rank knelt and took up the aiming position while the third rank moved to the gaps between the men in the second. All cocked their muskets, upon which the command *t'an* was given (short for *schlagt an* – take aim). This was the signal for the second and third ranks to step back with the right foot, transferring the weight of their bodies to the left and at the same time bring down their muskets to the aim. On the command *feuer* (fire), all three ranks pulled their triggers. Immediately they had fired, they pulled down their weapons in front of their stomachs, the front rank sprang up and the other two closed up their right feet. All then loaded and when ready, shouldered their arms. When all were standing shouldered and thus easily visible through the fog of powder smoke, their officer could see that the platoon was again ready to fire.

Oddly enough for the nation that claimed military predominance, the French persistently clung to older methods. At the beginning of the war their basic formation was five ranks, decreased to four after 1706. The entire grenadier company occupied the right of the line followed by the colonel's company and then the other companies in order of their captains' seniority. The extreme left was formed by the picquet which was a composite flank guard formed by four men from the first four companies and three each from the remaining eight, plus two sergeants and a drummer.

This formation naturally meant that not all ranks could fire at once, especially as the French did not employ any form of echeloning their files – each man stood directly behind the other! In fact, only three ranks could fire at all. If a concentrated volley was required, the front rank knelt, the second crouched and the third stood while the remaining two did nothing.

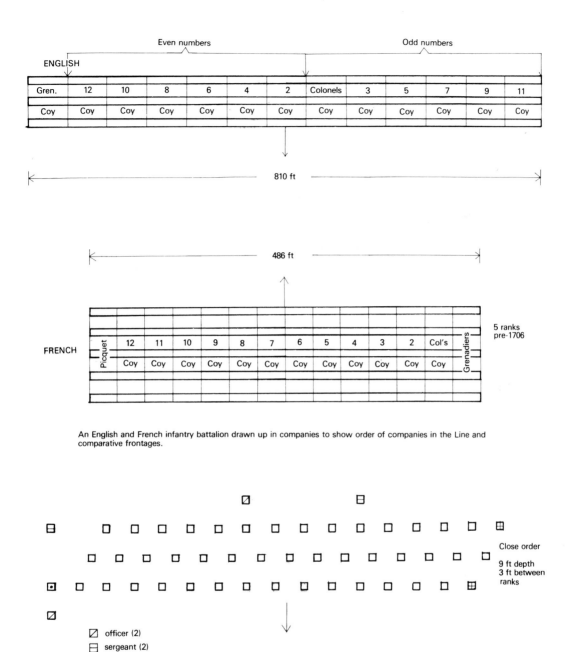

ENGLISH

	Even numbers						Odd numbers				
Gren.	12	10	8	6	4	2	Colonels	3	5	7	9	11
Coy	Coy	Coy	Coy	Coy	Coy	Coy	Coy	Coy	Coy	Coy	Coy	Coy

|← 810 ft →|

|← 486 ft →|

FRENCH

| Picquet | 12 | 11 | 10 | 9 | 8 | 7 | 6 | 5 | 4 | 3 | 2 | Col's | Grenadiers |
| | Coy | Coy | Coy | Coy | Coy | Coy | Coy | Coy | Coy | Coy | Coy | Coy | |

5 ranks pre-1706

An English and French infantry battalion drawn up in companies to show order of companies in the Line and comparative frontages.

Close order

9 ft depth
3 ft between ranks

☑ officer (2)
⊟ sergeant (2)
⊞ corporal (2)
⊡ drummer (1)
☐ private (40)

An English infantry platoon in close order, loaded and ready to fire.

Fig. 30.   French and English Infantry formations.

Therefore the much older systems were retained in some cases. In firing by files, two complete files (ten men) would move out a few paces, spread out into a line, fire and then march back into place to be followed by the next group. This was courting disaster by loosening the strength of the line, and anyway, it meant that too few shots could be applied at any one time. Therefore, various methods of firing by ranks was resorted to. One way was for the front rank to fire and then drop to the ground, being followed by the other four in turn. When

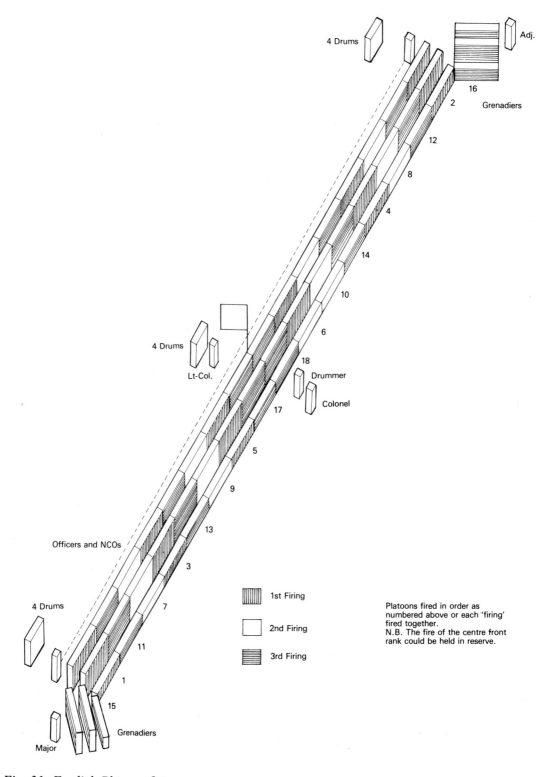

Fig. 31. English Platoon firing system.

50

all had fired, those that were still alive scrambled to their feet and started to load. An alternative was for the front four ranks to kneel while the rear rank fired, after which the others stood up in turn.

All the above schemes were difficult to control, and without iron discipline would soon have become ragged. Besides, by forming up in five or four ranks, a French battalion occupied a much shorter front than the equivalent English unit (in four ranks, 486 ft to 810 ft).

Captain Parker was firmly convinced of the relative methods – '. . . the manner of our firing was different from their's; the French at all times fired by ranks, which can never do equal execution with our platoon firing, especially when six platoons are fired together.'[18] In this connexion he is referring to an encounter in the woods at Malplaquet (1709) when his Irish regiment became entangled with an Irish unit in French service. 'When we had advanced within a hundred paces of them, they gave us a fire of one of their ranks; whereupon we halted, and returned them the fire of our six platoons at once; and immediately made ready the six platoons of our second fire, and advanced upon them again. They then gave us the fire of another rank, and we returned them a second fire, which made them shrink; however, they gave us the fire of a third rank after a scattering manner, and then retired into the wood in great disorder: on which we sent our third fire after them, and saw them no more.' The result of this engagement according to the author was four 'English' Irish killed and six wounded while the 'French' Irish lost nearly forty. The irony is that some six hundred bullets only managed to disable forty opponents!

So far we have described basic evolutions in attack, but close-quarter fighting was seldom indulged in. Once the enemy had been disorganised by artillery and point-blank volleys of musketry, the cavalry closed in to start the rout. It was in such a situation that discipline sorted out the good units from the bad.

When forced to retreat, a battalion that was still in good order faced about and marched off, followed by the colonel and his drummer. If the pursuers started to get too close, the colonel would order the next firing to turn and fire a volley, while the rest continued their withdrawal. This firing then doubled back and reloaded within the safety of the line, while the next group turned and faced the enemy.

If a line presented an unbroken front, it was extremely difficult for cavalry to attack them, but with all the bayonets and muskets pointing to the front, they were extremely vulnerable from the rear. Once a line started to retreat, gaps would inevitably appear through which the horse could gallop, and then there was only one way for a battalion to save itself – to form a defensive *carrée* or square.

To do this, an evolution was carried out based on the Grand Divisions or groupings of three musket companies. One division (the one nearest the enemy) stood fast while the other three marched back and round to form the square. The drummers and the colours sheltered in the centre while the grenadiers split into four groups to strengthen the corners. The two battalion guns could also take position in front of the most threatened face. Under these circumstances, the platoon system was abandoned and firing was by ranks along a complete face.

The square would normally stand and fight at the halt, but if enemy attacks slackened off, it could continue to retreat without breaking formation. The two side flanks simply turned in the direction of march and the rear face made an about turn. The grenadiers stayed behind to act as rearguard or 'forlorn hope'.

Kane commented: '. . . If a body of Foot have but Resolution to keep their Order, there is no Body of Horse dare venture within their fire.'[19]

The foregoing has been but a summary of basic infantry tactics, and for their practical applications the reader should study the many accounts of the battles of the period. As at any time in history, the performance of a unit depended mainly on the quality of its officers

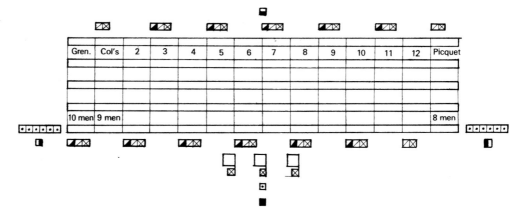

Gren.	Col's	2	3	4	5	6	7	8	9	10	11	12	Picquet
10 men	9 men												8 men

French battalion of 13 companies in 5 rank line of battle. 5 ranks
each of about 130 men. Total, 650 NCOs and men plus some 40 officers.

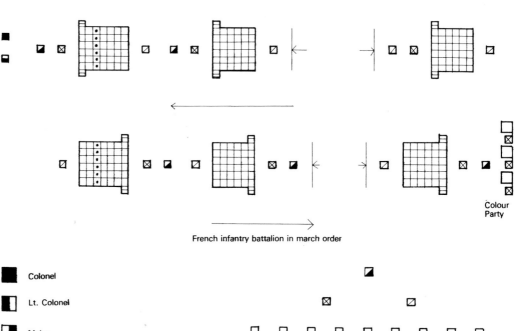

French infantry battalion in march order

Colour
Party

■	Colonel
◨	Lt. Colonel
◻	Major
◪	Captain
◿	Lieutenant
⊠	Sous-lieutenant or ensign
⊟	Sergeant
▢	Privates
⊡	Drummers

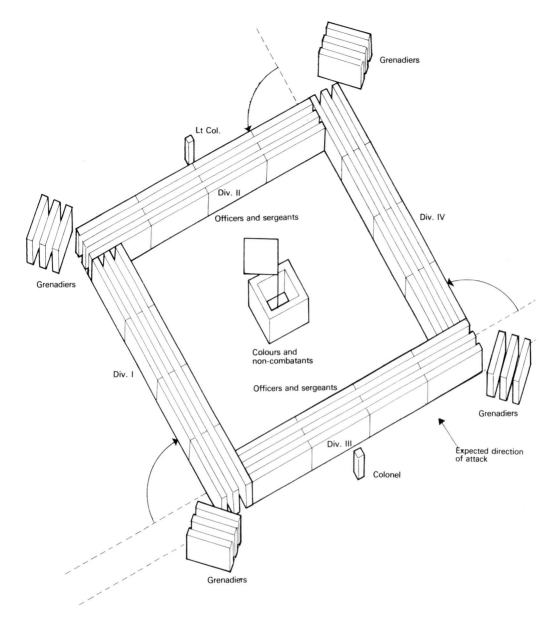

Grenadiers

Lt Col.

Div. II

Officers and sergeants

Div. IV

Grenadiers

Colours and
non-combatants

Officers and sergeants

Grenadiers

Div. I

Div. III

Expected direction
of attack

Colonel

Grenadiers

Fig. 33. Above, *infantry battalion forming a square. 4 'Grand Divisions' each of four platoons.*

Fig. 32. Left, *French infantry company. Firing by company – front four ranks kneel. Rear fires and then the others in order. Firing by rank – front kneels, second crouches and third stands. All fire together. Rear two ranks held as reserve.*

and nco's. Some regiments achieved magnificent records in combat, while others broke under fire and fled. It took great courage to face your enemy at sixty paces, with your comrades falling on either side, and to go through the motions of loading and firing like a machine.

In conclusion, I have often been asked why they did not lie down and take cover while firing – to which there is a simple but not so obvious answer. The reason is that with their long muzzle-loaders, they could not operate the ramrod in the prone position. Only the advent of the breech-loading rifle permitted the infantry to blend into their surroundings.

NOTES

1 For details of muskets of the period, see Blackmore, *British Military Firearms*, 28 et seq.
2 Eckhardt-Morawietz. 13.
3 Ibid. 22.
4 Various. *Die Schlacht bei Minden*. 68n.
5 Saxe. Vol. I, 40.
6 For a full list of battles during the period covered by this book, see Chandler, *Art of War*, Appendix II.
7 Parker. 89.
8 Fortescue. Vol. I, 329.
9 Blackmore. Op. cit. 31.
10 Mackay. *Memoirs of the Scottish War*. 1833. 52.
11 Quoted by Blackmore. Op. cit. 42.
12 Susane. Vol. I, 271.
13 John Evelyn. *Diary*. 26 June 1678.
14 Colonie. 170.
15 For a brief survey, see Chandler, op. cit., 98 et seq.
16 Scouller. Appendix E.
17 Anon. *System of Camp Discipline etc.*
18 Parker. 89.
19 Kane. 123.

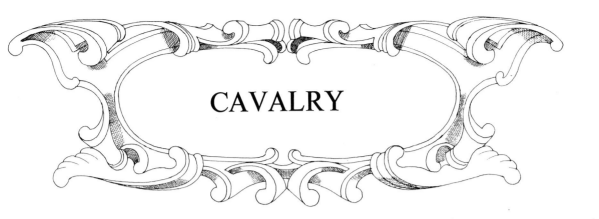

CAVALRY

All the armies of the period under consideration had a mounted arm, and as an average the proportion of cavalry was about one-third of the total number of troops. During the course of the eighteenth century, this proportion tended to decrease, until during the Napoleonic period it amounted to around 15 per cent.[1] Throughout the eighteenth century (and still today) the cavalry tended to regard themselves as the predominant arm, a throwback to their élite role in mediaeval warfare.

Naturally there were valid reasons for this decline in representation, the main one being the simple matter of cost – horsemen were tending more and more to become an expensive luxury. There was not only the trooper to feed and equip, but his horse as well – in terms of relative cost you could have three infantrymen for the price of one trooper. However, in an aristocratic age cavalry still signified prestige, and the resources had to be found to maintain them. In time of war, it was far simpler to raise a battalion of foot and equip it than to produce a troop of horsemen from scratch.

A good charger cost £15 at the beginning of the eighteenth century, and this was a vulnerable investment – horses were easily wounded or killed in action, were accident prone, and subject to a whole variety of illnesses. Thus the question of remounts was one with which the cavalry commander was constantly confronted during a campaign.

The mounting system in the English army was as follows. A man's horse was regarded basically as his own property. In some cases recruits brought their own horses with them, and if they left the service honourably, they were entitled to take a horse with them. If the recruit did not have a suitable animal, he was supplied with one and its cost was deducted from his pay. The problem was that if he lost the animal for any number of reasons and could not replace it from his own pocket, he ceased to be a cavalryman. To obviate this situation, a code of regulations was published in 1697 which stipulated that each man was to be stopped 4 shillings per week during the summer, or 'grass', months when the bulk of the fodder was free. This money was to be devoted to remounting, and thus the horses became in effect the common property of the troop.[2]

An ordinary trooper was paid subsistence at the rate of 2 shillings daily, half of which was regarded as being for feeding his animal. The rest was to feed himself, maintain his equipment and shoe his horse, and the equivalent rate was 6 pence for an infantry private. Horse-shoes were bought by the government in bulk and supplied to the individual regiments for cash.

In all fairness, however, the government paid for horses killed in battle, only those dying from natural causes or through negligence having to be replaced by the men themselves. The worst slaughter of horses took place during sea passages. Conyngham's Dragoons, who sailed from Ireland to the Peninsula in 1704, set off

Fig. 34. *French household cavalry. Trooper of the* Garde du Corps *and a* Mousquetaire. *Note the butt of the carbine in the saddle boot. Engraving by N. Guerard.*

with 286 horses, 141 of which died en route.[3]

Apart from the question of expense, the other main reason for the gradual decline in the number of cavalry maintained was the change in weapons and the resulting different tactics. The demise of the pike meant that any given army had far more infantrymen in the line aiming guns – changing them from a defensive role of warding off cavalry to an active one of shooting at horses. The resulting heavy casualties must have discouraged commanders, and as a result, the role of the cavalry in action became restricted to administering the final blow to the enemy – after the infantry had managed to shatter the opposing formations.

TYPES OF CAVALRY

In the same way as the infantry, the armies of the early eighteenth century contained a number of different types of mounted soldier which again produced problems of a semantic nature – different names meant different things in various languages. The following sections list the main types of horse and their weapons and equipment.

THE HORSE

This was the name applied to the cavalry element of the royal guards and the bulk of the mounted regiments in any army of the period, although the individual units rejoiced in a variety of names.

In theory, cuirassier regiments were heavy cavalry reserved for shock action in battle and protected by varying amounts of body armour. This title was popular in Germany and Austria, but in terms of armament and equipment the cuirassier was little different from the English trooper. Most of the latter were organised into units known simply as 'Regiments of Horse' to distinguish them from the similarly equipped Household Cavalry.

The French household troops, collectively referred to as the *Maison du Roi* were made up from a variety of different units – the two companies of *Mousquetaires*, the *Gendarmes*

Fig. 35. French cavalry. Gendarme *and* chevaux légers. *N. Guerard.*

de la Garde, the *Gardes du Corps* and a company of *Grenadiers à Cheval*. The latter, as their name implied, were grenadiers mounted on horseback, and the English Household Cavalry also had troops of Horse Grenadier Guards.

Another French unit with royal bodyguard status was the Gendarmerie, while the remainder of the cavalry were termed *Chevaux-Légers* – literally, light horse.[4] This was simply to distinguish them from the *Maison du Roi* and the *Gendarmerie* and did not signify that they were 'light' in the sense of being auxiliary cavalry to be found in some armies of the period. Another term used by the French was *Carabinier* to denote troops armed with blunderbusses (see Glossary) rather than the normal carbine.

WEAPONS

Treating the bulk of European cavalry in general terms, their weapons and equipment were remarkably similar, consisting of carbine, pistols and a sword. The following is a broad description of the characteristics of these weapons without any attempt at classifying the many national peculiarities.

The carbine was simply a short-barrelled musket with a bore somewhat smaller than that of the normal infantry weapon. As its inherent characteristics were the same as the latter, the remarks in the previous chapter about accuracy and design equally apply. It was carried on a sling worn over the left shoulder, as if a full-length musket had been used on horseback, it would have been more or less impossible to load. To get the ramrod into the end of the muzzle, this would have had to be lowered to such an extent that the butt would have been almost on the ground, dangling from an over-long sling. An additional reason for a short-barrelled weapon was that to load it, it had to be transferred from the right to the left of the saddle, to allow the trooper to operate the ramrod with his right hand (assuming that he was not left-handed). A full-length weapon would have been too unwieldy under the circumstances.

Therefore as a result of experience, carbines were developed for cavalry use with a barrel length of between two and a half and three feet.

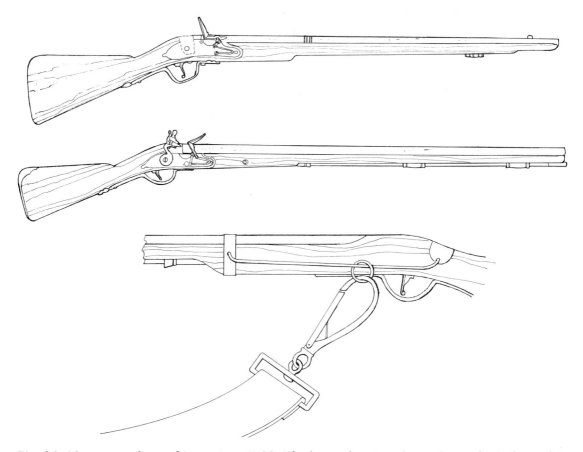

Fig. 36. Above, *cavalry carbines, circa 1700. The lower drawing shows the method of attaching the sling with the carbine hook moving along the slide.*
Fig. 37. Right, *cavalry pistols.* Top, *English circa 1700.* Centre, *French 1700.* Lower, *Austrian early eighteenth century.*

By 1700, all the various armies used flintlock carbines constructed in a similar fashion and specially adapted for mounted use.

When riding, the weapon was carried suspended from its sling and with one end resting in a leather bucket slung from the right-hand side of the saddle – there are contemporary illustrations showing both butt and muzzle inserted into the boot. It was attached to the sling by a spring hook so that it could be easily and quickly removed. This hook was known in German as a *karabiner haken* or carbine hook, and is the origin of the carabiner used by mountaineers.

On the side of the carbine itself was a metal slide about one foot long, along which a ring could travel – the hook was attached to this,

which gave sufficient movement for the weapon to be swung over the saddle in front of the rider.

In combat, the carbine was strictly a one-shot, short-range weapon. Once loaded it could be discharged by a horseman advancing at walking pace, but he (and his whole formation) then had to stop to load. If we then consider the inaccuracy of the musket at sixty paces, fired by men firmly planted on the ground, it is hardly surprising that a carbine fired by a man in the saddle, using both hands and mounted on a horse probably made skittish by the noise and smoke of battle, was not a lot of use. A 1672 treatise recommended that they be fired at an opposing horseman at a range of 12 feet! Once he had discharged his piece, the trooper simply

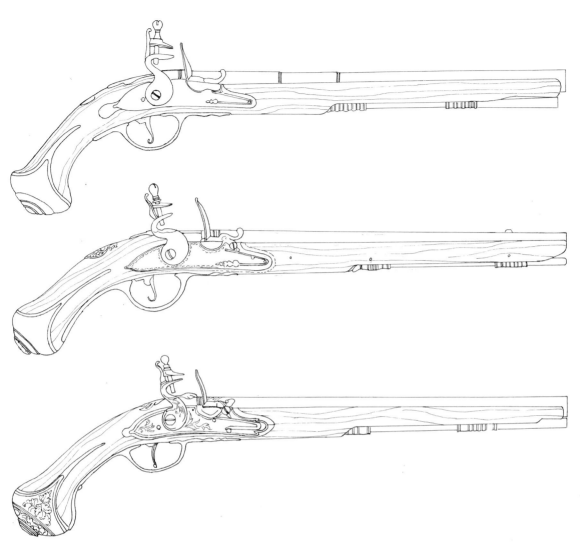

dropped it and drew his sword, leaving it to dangle from the end of the sling.

To load, the trooper recovered his carbine and lifted it so that the butt rested on his right thigh and held with the left (or bridle) hand. He then pulled the cock back to the half or safety position and primed the pan, not forgetting to close the cover afterwards! Next, the carbine was transferred to the left side of the saddle and lowered as far as the sling would reach. Supporting the weapon with his left hand, the trooper then inserted the cartridge and went through the complicated motions of drawing out the ramrod, turning it, shortening his grip, etc. Woe betide him if he dropped something in the heat of the moment. Once these operations had been safely performed, he pulled the carbine over to the right side again and rested it on his thigh, pointing upwards, ready to fire.

When he wanted to fire, he pulled the cock fully back and 'presented' the weapon. To do this he could either drop the reins and fire in the normal way with both hands, or with the carbine pressed into his right shoulder, he could rest it on his bridle arm and shoot across the head of his horse from right to left.

In addition to their carbine, most European cavalry were equipped with a pair of pistols carried in wooden or leather holsters on either side of the front of the saddle. These too used the flintlock principle and had a barrel length from 10 to 14 inches. The ordinary private troopers had pistols with wooden shafts furnished with plain brass or steel fittings, but the more wealthy officers could indulge themselves with finely wrought and decorated weapons.

The Comte de Mérode-Westerloo who certainly was not as hard up as he constantly complained, wrote: 'I purchased some fine pistols to replace the four or five pairs I had lost on my horses at Blenheim. Each horse's holsters, saddle and harness, pistols and other equipment cost me a cool thousand crowns.'[5]

The average pistol was a 24 bore (24 balls to the pound), and an interesting feature is that they were usually fired on their side with the lock uppermost. The reason for this was that as the priming pan was on the side with the touch-hole running down into the chamber, if the pan was not properly filled, the motion of the horse might cause it to spill. By holding it on its side, the powder naturally covered the touch-hole, reducing the chances of a misfire.

However, this caused in turn a ballistic deviation. With the pistol held in the normal upright way, it recoiled upwards. On its side it would recoil to the trooper's left, who therefore had to offset his aim to the right – taking care not to blow off his horse's head in the process.

The method of use was as follows:

'Uncap your pistols' (uncover them).
'Draw your pistols – this must be performed with the right hand, the left pistol first, and then mount the muzzle.'
(Note: the left hand was supposedly holding the reins. Mounting the muzzle meant to rest it on the thigh.)

If not loaded, this was then carried out, followed by:

'Present your pistols.'
'Give fire. In firing of your pistols you are not to fire directly forwards, to your enemies horses head, but toward the right hand with the lock of your pistol upwards.'
'Return your pistol.'

Such pistols were naturally inaccurate except at extremely short ranges and their uses were limited. If they were regarded as a defence against surprise attack, they had to be kept loaded in their holsters ready for immediate use. However, the motion of the horse could easily set them off – certainly scorching and possibly wounding the poor animal in the process. Besides which, unless the ball was firmly stuffed in with its paper wad, it would fall out into the bottom of the holster, followed by the charge of powder.

Marlborough certainly did not think much of firearms, as he 'would allow the Horse but three charges of powder and ball for each man for a campaign, and that only for guarding their horses when at grass and not to be made use of in action.'[6]

The relative use of firearms and swords by cavalry will be discussed later under the heading of tactics, but the swords themselves require a brief mention. Again, no accurate classification is possible owing to the lack of standardisation – most swords were purchased and issued on a regimental basis, as well as the fact that some troopers would have been armed with personal or family weapons.

However, the swords used by European cavalry units were all, broadly speaking, similar in design and shape. Known collectively as the broadsword, they featured a basket hilt made of steel, comprising a number of bars to enclose the hand of the user. The blade was straight, double edged and tapered to a point, making it both a cut and a thrust weapon. To improve the grip, it was normal to bind it with serrated silver wire, and a loop or sword knot was attached to the pommel through which the trooper could place his wrist to avoid dropping it in the heat of action.

Swords were worn on the left of the body, suspended from the waist belt in a frog, and bayonets were not issued to line cavalry. A contemporary instruction states that:

'the souldier [having fired his pistol] . . . is to take himself to the use of the sword, [his sword being drawn and placed in his bridle hand] and having received it into his weapon hand for service, must

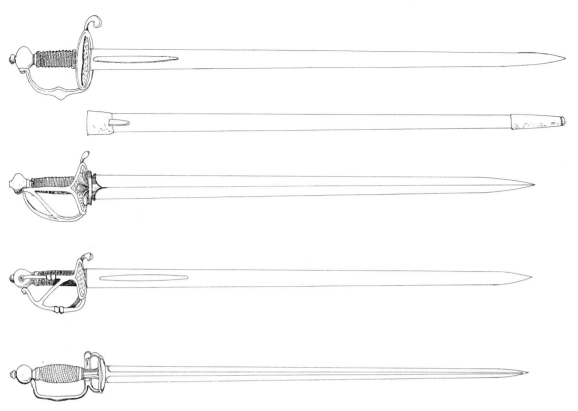

Fig. 38. French cavalry swords. Top, *'Walloon' broadsword, circa 1685.* Centre, *two broadswords, circa 1700.* Bottom, épee *1700.*

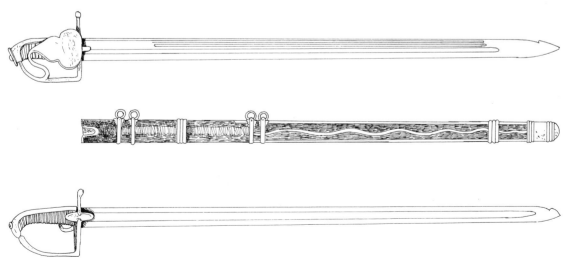

Fig. 39. Top, *Austrian heavy cavalry broadsword with scabbard, early eighteenth century.* Bottom, *Austrian cuirassier broadsword, same date.*

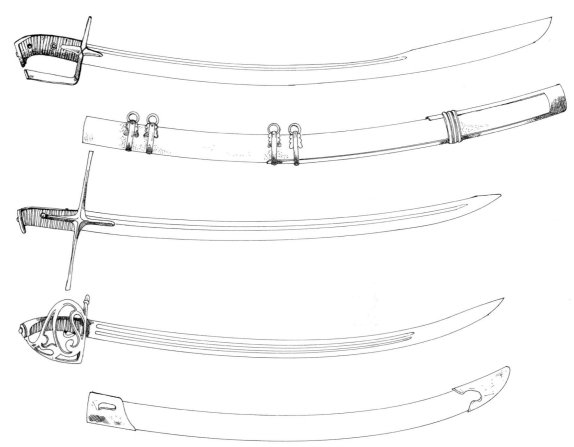

Fig. 40. Hussar sabres, early eighteenth century, top *and* centre. Bottom, *Austrian horse grenadier sabre, circa 1700.*

place the pummel [sic] upon his right thigh and so to raise his point to his mark, high or lower, as occasion serveth and therewith endeavour to disable his enemy either by cutting his horse's bridle or other [wise] his arms, that he serveth in, which if discreetly managed will prove peril to them.'

Reading the various extracts quoted above, one comes to the conclusion that the cavalry were extremely good horsemen. They had to constantly shift their various weapons from hand to hand and still control their mounts – in conformity with the rest of their unit. Such drills were all very well when carried out for a parade review, but must have been extremely difficult under combat conditions.

EQUIPMENT

As in the case of the infantry, this varied enormously from nation to nation and from regiment to regiment. However, there were certain basic trends that can be identified.

Body armour varied according to the type of unit and national preference. Not all cuirassier regiments wore cuirasses! In the French and Austrian armies, the heavy cavalry retained the full cuirass (back and breast plate), and in some units iron gauntlets were still worn. How they managed their weapons remains a mystery. A full cuirass was fastened together by straps passing over each shoulder and locating in studs welded on to the breastplate. A further strap passed around the waist and buckled at the front. Some cuirasses ended at the waist, while others were slightly flared out at the base to

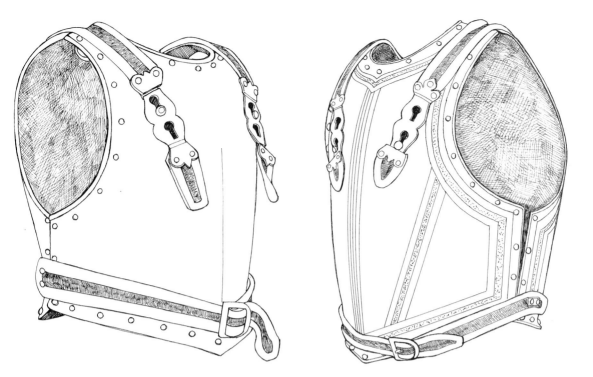

Fig. 41. French cuirasses from the reign of Louis XIV. Left, the plainer soldiers' pattern. Right, officers' pattern. Note the fastening system.

enable some of the weight to be supported on the hips.

The Swedish cavalry wore no armour at all, as was the case with the English prior to 1707. It was then that Marlborough ordered the reissue of breastplates, on account of the heavy casualties caused by French pistol fire, and he persuaded the Dutch to do likewise.[7]

Like most things in life, armour had its advantages and disadvantages. The added protection it gave against the improved firearms had to be balanced against the loss of speed and mobility occasioned by the extra weight. Marlborough issued only the breastplate, for the obvious reason that a man armoured at the back as well as the front might be more inclined to run away.

Methods of wearing the cuirass/breastplate naturally differed. The various German armies tended to retain the buff leather coat and wore their armour on top. Buff leather had a suede-like texture and was proof against sword cuts. Such garments had been popular in England during the Civil War for cavalry, but by 1700 had been replaced by the traditional red full-skirted coat. When the breastplate was reintroduced in 1707, it was worn by English and Dutch troops *underneath* the coat and thus cannot be seen in contemporary paintings.

The only armies to retain helmets were the Bavarian and some Austrian regiments. They wore steel helmets of the 'lobster pot' variety with a face guard of metal bars and fish-scale neck plates – remarkably similar to those worn by Cromwell's Ironsides. Other countries had adopted the basic tricorn hat as being the ideal form of headgear, although horse grenadier regiments wore the mitre cap. This is one of the anomalies of the period, as the basic reason for the appearance of the mitre cap was that grenadiers had to be able to sling their muskets and thus tended to knock off their hats. The same, however, applied to cavalry with their slung carbines, but who nevertheless retained the tricorn.

'Iron secrets' were popular as a form of extra

Fig. 42. Marlborough's horse held by a servant. Detail from a painting by James Ross (1715 ?) purporting to be of the Battle of Ramillies. This shows the comparatively simple harness of the period.

head protection, and consisted of a metal skull cap worn underneath the hat to protect against sword blows. During the 1703 campaign in Bavaria, de la Colonie wrote in his memoirs:

> 'I put to the test in this battle a small frame of well-tempered iron, which the cavalry officers, not in the cuirassiers, were in the habit of placing in the crown of their hats. It certainly saved me from the effects of two heavy sabre cuts . . . to the extent that I got off with merely a few bruises.'[8]

In this respect it should be noted that de la Colonie was in Bavarian service, hence his reference to cuirassiers, who naturally wore helmets – he himself commanded a foot grenadier regiment.

To protect the legs, thigh boots of thick leather were worn, turned over at the top and specially strengthened around the feet. These

were commonly referred to as *gambadoes* or jack boots,[9] and it is clear that the latter expression did not have any evil connotations as it does today. They were further embellished with spurs – plain for the troopers and often extremely ornate for senior officers. There is a pair of such boots preserved in the Bavarian Army Museum at Ingolstadt which resemble those worn by a modern diver, and they must have rendered a trooper more or less immobile on foot.

Once the trooper was dressed, he had to put on his sword belt on which he would have carried his ammunition pouch – filled with cartridges for both carbine and pistols. Over his left shoulder came the broad carbine sling made of leather and some 5 inches wide. Instead of a sling haversack, he carried his belongings in a valise, a cylindrical container, strapped behind

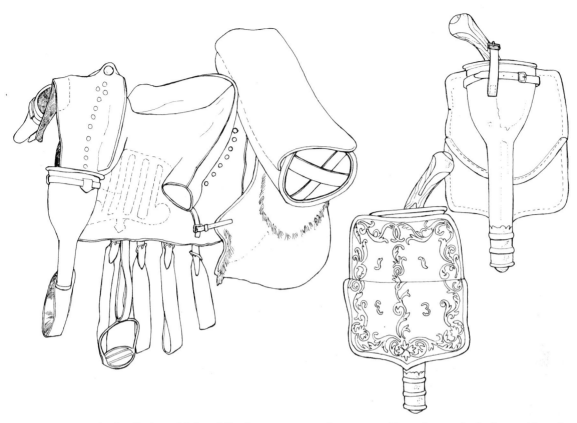

Fig. 43. Left, *the 'Killiekrankie' saddle, late seventeenth century. Note the method of attaching the pistol holsters and the valise.* Right, *inside and outside views of a pistol in a wooden holster covered by an ornamental 'cape'.*

the saddle. Finally, gauntlets of buff leather were issued to protect the hands. Cavalry are normally depicted wearing gauntlets, which would have been useful for riding and for sword fighting, but I find it difficult to understand how they could have operated firearms with their hands encased in stiff gloves. Drill manuals make no mention of them being discarded when loading or firing, which would have been extremely difficult under the circumstances.

The saddles of the period were of padded leather raised both at the back and front to give the trooper support when fighting. Provision was made for attaching the holsters and the carbine boot. The former were normally covered by embroidered and fringed fabric skirts, and a housing was worn underneath the saddle. In English service these were normally the same colour as the regimental facings and trimmed with gold lace and the regimental arms or emblem. Senior officers, however, could sport furnishings of embroidered silk or brocade, and the National Army Museum has a set reputed to have belonged to Marlborough.

Stirrups were large iron affairs suitable for accommodating the heavy boots, and harness was fairly simple. Beside the usual bit, bridle and reins to control the animal, there was a crupper to hold the tail, a girth under the saddle, a breast strap and a martingale. There again, ornateness was determined by money, and senior officers are often portrayed on finely outfitted horses.

DRAGOONS

Dragoons were literally mounted infantry – or

65

Fig. 44. Left, *a French dragoon*, right, *a cavalry trooper. The dragoon's horse is smaller and he is wearing a stocking cap Instead of boots, his legs are protected by gaiters. Guerard engraving.*

cavalry who fought on foot, and used their horse purely to give them a measure of mobility. Thus their animals tended to be smaller and cheaper than the chargers of the line cavalry. Their name probably originated from the fact that earlier in the seventeenth century they were commonly armed with the 'dragon'. This was a short barrelled carbine with the full bore of a musket – similar to a blunderbuss or musketoon. Their title, however, had certain sinister overtones in that they were often used in France for coercing the civilian population – hence the *dragonnades*, the billeting of unruly soldiers on disobedient citizens.

It is certain that dragoons, at least in the English army, suffered from a lack of prestige in comparison with line cavalry, by whom they were regarded as an offshoot of the infantry. This was reflected in the scales of pay and subsistence. Naturally, the dragoon's inferior horse was expected to eat less, and the 1704 Mutiny Act laid down weekly subsistence rates for a cavalry trooper of 14s., and 8s. 2d. for a dragoon private.[10]

A dragoon was armed with a carbine, but as he fought on foot, he had a bayonet as well but no pistols. His sword was of the heavier cavalry variety, and in some armies axes were carried.

In terms of uniform, dragoons looked like infantry wearing heavy riding boots. They never wore armour, and sported the inevitable tricorn hat and long coat, with the cartridge pouch on the waist belt or hung from a shoulder strap.

The problem was that they were neither one thing nor the other. Their heavy boots hindered their mobility on the ground, and when going into action, numbers of men had to be detached as horse-holders. On the other hand, their inferior horses meant that they were unable to hold their own in mounted combat.

However, their numbers *vis à vis* heavy cavalry tended to increase during the course of the eighteenth century. The reason for this, apart from their relative cheapness, was their all-round nature, as they could be used for a variety of guard duties as well as such tasks as demolishing fortifications.

Fig. 45. Hussards royaux *after Guerard. Note the heads on the swords! The flamboyant uniforms were to appear in all armies later in the eighteenth century. Axes were carried slung from the saddle.*

LIGHT HORSE

This type of cavalry originated from the irregular formations raised in Eastern Europe – the Russian Cossacks, the Hungarian Hussars, Croatian Pandours, etc. – and by the middle of the eighteenth century such units formed a stable component of the mounted arm of any army. At the beginning of the century, however, they only found limited acceptance, being generally viewed with suspicion as little better than bandits and brigands.

There were no light cavalry formations in the English army, but various continental countries made tentative steps to raise such units. The Hapsburgs with their history of war against the Turks and Hungarians, had made a start in 1688 by raising regiments of Hungarians, known as Hussars. By retaining their native costume of tight frogged jackets, skin-tight breeches and the fur-trimmed dolman slung over the shoulder, they were to set a fashion of military splendour that was to be all the rage a century later.

The French adopted similar units during the War of the Spanish Succession, but other nations hesitated for some years. English Hussars developed from light dragoon regiments, making their appearance in mid-century.

These Eastern Europeans brought with them the curved sabre that was to gradually oust the broadsword as the standard cavalry weapon.

CAVALRY ORGANISATION

Here again we come up against the virtual impossibility of being able to lay down any standard formations, and have to make do with examples in order to create a general impression. If we assume that cavalry made up roughly one-third of any given army at the beginning of the eighteenth century, dragoons formed varying proportions of that total. In the Russian army they were decidedly in the majority as they were in the English army, although in the late seventeenth-century campaigns in Flanders the reverse had been true.

As in the case of the infantry, the basic unit

67

was the regiment, more or less owned by its colonel, although this was purely an administrative formation. A regiment was sub-divided into varying numbers of troops, roughly corresponding to the infantry company, as well as a small headquarters staff. For tactical purposes, these troops were grouped together in units of between two and four, to form squadrons. When describing numbers present at a particular battle, contemporary sources always refer to squadrons and not to regiments.

In combat, the squadrons were often grouped together to form brigades of a temporary nature. The Brigadier-General had official army rank, but was usually also the colonel of the senior regiment represented in the brigade. He would have a small staff, but this was an *ad hoc* device and did not feature on any official establishment.

In view of their odd status, the dragoons organised their troops into companies rather than squadrons.

Actual numbers varied enormously, both as far as official establishments were concerned and actually as determined by finance and campaign losses. In English units there is the added complication of widows' men and officers' servants appearing on the muster rolls. In an effort to give a general guide, David Chandler quotes an average figure of fifty officers and men for a cavalry troop,[11] thus giving a three-troop squadron a strength of 150, and a typical regiment total of between 300 and 450. Having said that, however, we must look at some sample establishments.

During peacetime, numbers were generally allowed to fall drastically – the average twelve-troop French regiment had only thirty-six troopers in 1701. During the War of the Spanish Succession, the Austrians also had twelve-troop regiments which were paired into operational squadrons. In 1705, English horse regiments had an official troop strength of sixty and in 1702, the dragoons had fifty-four per company. By 1713, when we were pulling out of the war, these figures had reduced to thirty-six and thirty-eight respectively.

A troop was commanded by a captain assisted by a lieutenant and a cornet (equivalent to an infantry ensign). Instead of sergeants, there were three corporals of horse and one or two trumpeters. Among the officers on the establishment was a quartermaster, sometimes known as a *maréchal-des-logis*. Dragoons had a similar set-up – in line with cavalry practice, their junior subaltern was a cornet, but the senior nco's were sergeants and not corporals of horse. They also had drummers instead of trumpeters.

On duty, cavalry officers and nco's could only be distinguished from the common herd by their more ornate uniforms, as they naturally carried no staff weapons as symbols of office, and did not wear gorgets. French guards officers, however, carried ivory-tipped wooden wands as evidence of their superiority.

Broadly speaking, regimental headquarters staff in the various armies followed a similar pattern. The commanding officer was the colonel, who was in many cases also a general and thus an absentee. His deputy was a lieutenant-colonel, and the remaining staff officers were the major, adjutant, chaplain and surgeon, while some regiments could boast of a kettle drummer.

The above only applied to line cavalry and dragoon regiments. Élite bodyguard units frequently had a totally different establishment and even their own rank structures. The English Life Guards consisted of between three and four troops, each of 156 'private gentlemen' and had no separate regimental staff as the troops corresponded in strength to squadrons.

The term 'gentlemen' applied to Life Guard troopers implied that it was no disgrace for members of the upper classes to serve in the ranks of the monarch's bodyguard, and in the French *Gendarmerie* the troopers were styled *maîtres*. Peter Drake, who regarded himself as a gentleman, thought it no disgrace to serve in the latter, as he wandered from army to army in search of a commission.[12]

Each Life Guards troop had a captain in command, assisted by two lieutenants, a cornet

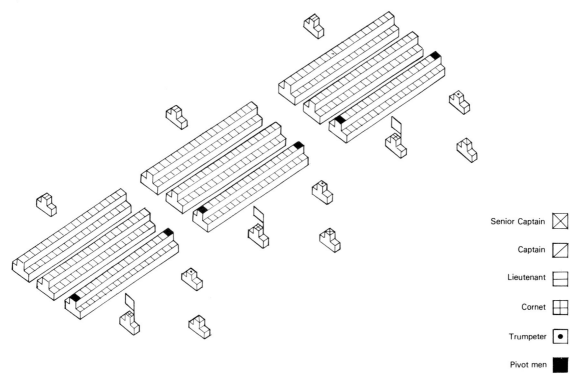

Senior Captain	⊠
Captain	◹
Lieutenant	⊟
Cornet	⊞
Trumpeter	⊡
Pivot men	◼

Fig. 46. Approximate line-up of a three troop cavalry squadron in three ranks, each troop comprising some 50 troopers. Open order – 6 ft between each horse and rank. Close order, 3 ft distances.

and four exempts. However, it is clear from the pay structure that the former ranks were equivalent to colonel and lieutenant-colonel, while the cornet and exempts were equal to captains. This may sound confusing, but they can best be referred to as dual ranks, i.e. captain and colonel, lieutenant and lieutenant-colonel, etc. A captain and colonel of Life Guards was paid 46s. daily in comparison to the 41s. of a line cavalry colonel, and so on down the scale.

In addition to those fulfilling command functions, each troop had an adjutant, surgeon and chaplain with officer status. The functions of sergeant and corporal were carried out by brigadiers and sub-brigadiers, who were in fact commissioned officers but should not be confused with brigadier-generals. Each troop also featured a kettle drummer and four trumpeters.

The Horse Grenadier Guards who were attached to the Life Guards had further individual peculiarities. The troops were commanded by a captain and colonel whose deputy was a lieutenant and lieutenant-colonel. They were followed by two lieutenants and captain and then a major, who was in fact junior to the lieutenants! The subalterns were a guidon and captain, and two sub-lieutenants, ranks which were only used in the Horse Grenadier Guards. There was the usual adjutant, chaplain and surgeon, and the nco's comprised six sergeants and six corporals. Instead of trumpets, each grenadier troop had four hautbois (see section on military music).

The issue was further complicated by a different establishment altogether for the Regiment of Royal Horse Guards, and so one can go on *ad infinitum*.[13] The structure of the various units of the French *Maison du Roi* was even more complicated and full of anomalies and exceptions which are not worth recounting here.[14]

69

TACTICAL EMPLOYMENT

Regarding the cavalry, Kane is tantalisingly brief. He simply said:

'It is sufficient for them to ride well, to have their horses well managed and trained up to stand fire; that they take particular notice of what part of the squadron they are in, their right and left hand men and file leaders, that they may when they happen to break readily know how to form. . . . That they march and wheel with a grace and handle their swords well, which is the only weapon our British Horse make use of when they charge the enemy; more than this is superfluous.'[15]

The main purpose of the cavalry in any army at the beginning of the eighteenth century was to fight the opposing horse, while at the same time the infantry were doing their best to disrupt their opposite numbers. Assuming that the cavalry managed to drive off their opponents, they could then reform and attend to the enemy infantry. We have seen that the role of the infantry was to supply static firepower, and the privilege of administering the *coup de grâce* was reserved for the horse. They alone usually decided the final outcome of a battle and the extent of the victory depended on their powers of pursuit.

If the maintenance of the line was all important for the infantry, the same applied to the cavalry formation, as stressed in the above extract from Kane. There was no room for individual action or small-scale use of initiative – only the mass could effect a decision.

Therefore, cavalry training depended firstly on teaching the men to operate as a composite body and to school their animals to do the same. As the squadron was the basic tactical unit, the manuals of the period refer mainly to formations required to be carried out by a group of some 150 men. In action, they were normally drawn up in two or three lines, commanded by the senior troop captain who sat in front accompanied by his trumpeter.

Within this formation when static, the men had to be able to perform the 'doublings' from open order (six feet between each horse both in rank and file) to close order (three feet distances). For the actual charge, they further reduced to 'close order from close order' by which the men moved together knee to knee in the ranks, and the files closed up until their horses were nose to tail.

Other 'postures' were facing about, counter-marching and wheeling. The latter depended upon the pivot men who stood still while the rest of the unit wheeled around them, each man having to know his exact place in the troop.

In addition to the above, however, the cavalry also had to carry out the various weapons exercises mentioned earlier, all without getting muddled up or dropping anything. Just imagine having to manage the reins and the sword with the left hand, while using the right hand to juggle with carbine and pistols. The dragoons had also to cope with the standard infantry drills when dismounted.

The use of cavalry on the battlefield was in a state of transition during the War of the Spanish Succession. The cavalry of the period had originated from the sixteenth-century German *Reiter*, who were heavily armoured horsemen equipped with firearms. They were developed to cope with pike formations – as these could not be charged, the cavalry had to stand off and fire at them. This idea of using horsemen as mobile firepower remained the staple idea throughout the seventeenth century and even into the eighteenth. Earlier, however, certain enterprising and far-sighted commanders had shown that shock action and cold steel were better. Gustavus Adolphus was the originator and he was emulated during the English Civil War both by Prince Rupert and by Oliver Cromwell.

What emerged was clearly a compromise. The French, who were still the foremost military nation at the end of the seventeenth century, used their cavalry initially as mounted musketeers. They trotted up in three lines to within range, and fired off their pistols and carbines. Only then did they take up their swords and engage the enemy at close quarters.

These tactics were emulated by the Austrians

Fig. 47. The Battle of Ramillies, by Laguerre. On the left is a cavalry skirmish and on the right, a trooper is using his pistol. In the background, a baggage train is being plundered.

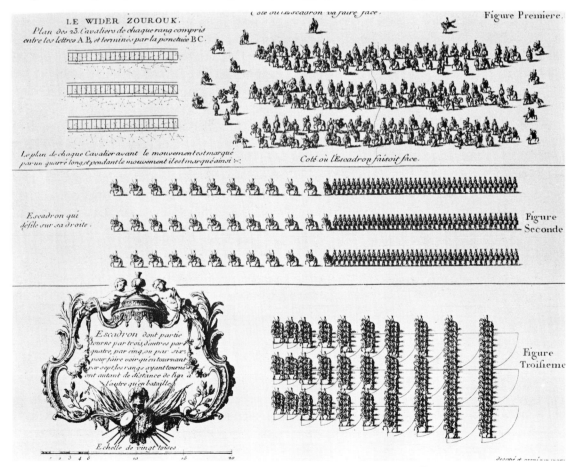

Fig. 48. French cavalry movements, circa 1700. Top, *the reassembly after battle.* Centre, *turning right from line into three files.* Bottom, *shortening from line into march column. From* Art de la Guerre *by Puysegur.*

and most of the smaller German armies, over which Marlborough had little influence. Where he had direct control, however, of the English and Dutch forces, he reintroduced the idea of relying on cold steel alone. We have already seen that he restricted ammunition issues to three rounds per man, only for use when guarding the horses at grass. He trained his cavalry to fight in twin squadron units drawn up in two lines and using only their swords. These charges, though, were only carried out at a smart trot or canter. The ultimate shock of a tight body of horsemen crashing in at the gallop was frowned upon owing to the difficulty of control – in the Marlborough campaigns nothing was allowed to disturb the sacred line formations. Thus much of the ultimate effectiveness was lost.

Another limiting factor was the comparative inability of Marlborough's cavalry to fully exploit a victory by means of a thorough pursuit – for which there were a number of reasons. Owing to the ever-present problem of desertion, no commander liked to see his men winging away on their own, and in Baroque warfare there was never that intense desire to utterly demolish a beaten enemy. The most vital factor, however, was that of simple logistics. After a battle there were prisoners to be rounded up and the whole army needed rest and recuperation. Exhausted horses had to be fed and fodder had to be gathered, bread had to be found for the men and there was plunder to be gathered in. In many ways it was far more rewarding to strip and search the dead than to chase after the living.

One exception was that errant contemporary of Marlborough's, Charles XII of Sweden, probably the greatest cavalry commander of the age. He too emphasised the value of the sword, but trained his horsemen to use speed as the ultimate weapon and to pursue their foes without respite.

However, Marlborough's greatness rests on his ability to see the broad picture of a campaign or battle rather than in the minutiae of tactics. Against the prevailing fashion he tended to hold in reserve a substantial portion of his cavalry in order to be able to use them at the decisive moment. Some generals have gone down in history as great infantry or cavalry commanders, but few like Marlborough have been able so skilfully to combine all the arms of their army into one battle winning entity.

The final word on the cavalry must rest with Eugene who inspected Marlborough's horse near Gross Heppach during the 1704 march to the Danube. 'My Lord', he is reported to have said, 'I never saw better horses, better clothes, finer belts and accoutrements; but money, which you don't want [for] in England, will buy clothes and fine horses, but it can't buy that lively air I see in every one of these troopers' faces'.[16]

NOTES

1 Chandler. *Art of War*. Table 38.
2 Walton. 709.
3 Scouller. 251.
4 See Chandler, op. cit. 33, for a discussion of this term.
5 Mérode-Westerloo. Chandler edition. 186.
6 Kane. *Discipline for Horse and Foot*.
7 Murray. *Dispatches*. Vol. iii. 309, 335, 461.
8 Colonie. 132.
9 Noyes. letter X. JSAHR. 1959.
10 Scouller. Appendix H.
11 Chandler. Op. cit. 45.
12 Drake. *Amiable Renegade*.
13 Scouller. Appendix E.
14 Chandler. Op. cit. 44.
15 Kane. *Campaigns*. 110.
16 Churchill. Vol i. 775, quoting from Hare's *Journal*.

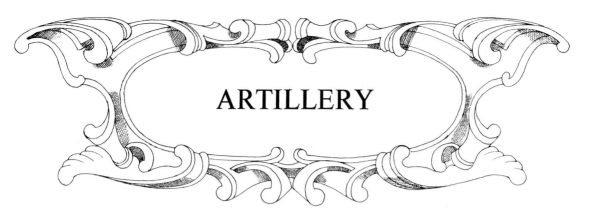

ARTILLERY

The first 'modern' army in which all three arms, the infantry, cavalry and artillery, operated together as a tactical entity and were paid from a central treasury was formed in 1494. In that year, Charles VIII of France invaded Italy, taking with him a train of artillery with the guns mounted on wheeled carriages, making them for the first time a mobile force which could accompany the rest of the army. From that date, the guns became an inseparable part of any army in the field. Although in the 200 years between Charles VIII and Marlborough certain detail improvements in artillery construction and practice became apparent, no sweeping changes were made. However, largely as a result of their experiences during the War of the Spanish Succession, various countries made serious efforts towards the middle of the eighteenth century to place their artillery establishments on a more regular basis.

In Marlborough's time there was no official sub-division of artillery into field and siege, although in practical terms these two basic classifications existed. In the field, the duties of the guns were to a certain extent passive – occasioned by poor mobility. Their tasks were to defend their own lines of cavalry and infantry and to try to break up the formations of the enemy. In fact, most battles started off with a mutual bombardment from the opposing sides' artillery as the troops formed up into line. During a siege, the heavy guns were sited so as to make a breach in the enemy's fortifications,

while the smaller guns picked off the defenders on the ramparts as well as being placed to drive off any attempt to attack the besiegers' lines.

In looking at the artillery arm during the early part of the eighteenth century we have to examine the actual weapons themselves, how they were operated and the personnel employed – bearing in mind the state of the technology of the period and the degree of organisation of which the various nations were capable. One authority has stated that the weapons were 'deficient alike in accuracy, in range, in penetrative power, and in durability'.[1]

Measured against modern capability of mass destruction this is true, but Marlborough and his contemporaries had to make do with what they had. They recognised the basic problems and did their best to cope with them.

At any time, there are certain basic criteria that have to be fulfilled if artillery is to be effective. Firstly, it must be mobile, both guns and their accompanying equipment on the road and over rough ground. If the guns cannot be brought into battle in time to support the troops, there is no point in carting them along. This poses a chicken-and-egg type problem – must the army slow down to keep pace with the guns, or must they be speeded up to march with the cavalry and infantry? Once on the battlefield, it is obvious that a high rate of fire is a necessity – preferably faster than the enemy's – and to achieve this, an adequate ammunition supply system must be devised. Finally, all the above

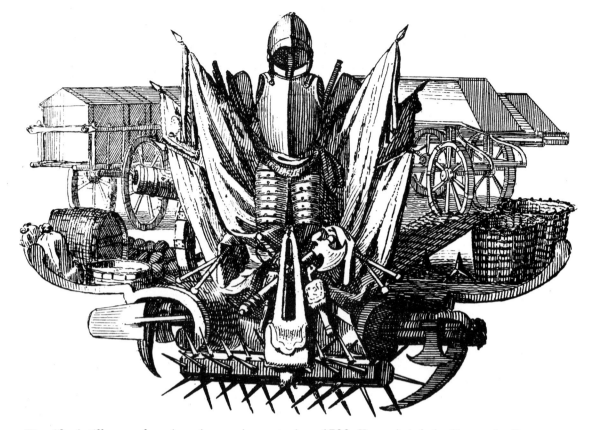

Fig. 49. Artillery and engineering equipment, circa 1700. From Art de la Guerre *by Puysegur.*

criteria having been achieved, they are rendered useless by inaccuracy and poor range – your weapons are useless unless they can deliver their load on the target.

It is clear that the above required a competent and professional organisation, and most armies of the period had an artillery arm that they could actually use with good effect – indeed, none of them would have been without their guns in action, although many complaints were made about the gunners and their equipment.

The basic problem was lack of mobility. On poor roads, vast numbers of horses were required to drag the cumbersome guns on their primitive wooden carriages, lurching from pot-hole to pot-hole. As they could not be speeded up the army perforce had to march to their pace. Frequent friction was caused by the fact that in many armies, the artillery was a separate semi-civilian organisation and that its waggons

and their drivers had to be procured from outside contractors or by impressment. As a result, campaigns tended to be fought where the ground was favourable and well supplied with roads and navigable rivers.

Technologically, nothing much could be done to improve the rate of fire until the advent of the modern breech-loading quick-firing guns. Well-drilled personnel helped to a certain extent, but weapon development was more or less at a standstill – the guns and their method of operation at Blenheim and Waterloo were basically similar.

The same applied to the vexed question of accuracy. As all the guns were smooth-bore muzzle-loaders, the same factors applied as have already been mentioned in connection with muskets – the necessary 'windage' creating ballistic instability. If we remember that the musket was inaccurate at 60 paces, a vast amount of ammunition had to be fired from a cannon in order to hit a target at 200 or even 500 paces. Therefore comparatively large numbers of guns were required to be massed in batteries in order to be effective, and this in turn led to the cumbersome trains and thus back to the problems of mobility.

THE WEAPONS

GENERAL

Three basic types were in use during the Marlborough period: the gun or cannon of various calibres, mounted on a wheeled carriage, which fired solid shot or canister at a limited degree of elevation; the mortar, mounted on a fixed bed and at a fixed angle of elevation, firing explosive shells at a high trajectory; the howitzer, which was basically a mobile mortar, mounted on a wheeled carriage, capable of being elevated up to 45 deg. and firing explosive shell or canister.

Before describing these in detail, it is worth looking at a few general principles. Their manufacture was a craft rather than a science which in the early days of gunfounding had developed from the methods used to cast church bells. We have seen that inventiveness had been applied with some success to hand weapons during the sixteenth and seventeenth centuries, but an experimental musket was cheap to produce and test — one man, a set of tools and a workbench were sufficient. A cannon required a vast amount of metal and a large crew to make, which in a period of small-scale industry did not invite speculative experimentation. There were plenty of inventors around, but Ordnance departments tended to look askance at such schemes. It was considered better to stick to tried and trusted principles rather than risk expensive failures.

The basic methods changed but little from the sixteenth to the nineteenth centuries. To cast a cannon, the first task was to make a clay replica of the piece complete with decorations, lifting lugs, trunnions, etc. This was coated with grease to stop it sticking to the clay mould which was then built up around it. When this was complete, the clay replica inside was broken up and removed piece by piece, leaving the mould to be baked solid.

This was then sunk into a pit dug directly beneath the furnace from which the metal to fill it would be tapped. To form the bore, a clay core was built up on a wooden former and placed down the centre line of the hollow mould. After the metal had been poured in at the muzzle end, the casting was left to cool off. To get the finished gun, the core and the mould had to be smashed. This meant in practice that no two guns were ever identical, and minor casting mistakes (such as the inexact alignment of the core) could not be subsequently corrected. All that could be done in the way of finishing was to ream out the bore, drill the touch-hole and file off any waste metal. It was not until the middle of the eighteenth century that a practical lathe was invented which was capable of drilling an accurate bore from a solid casting.[2]

The point that emerges from the above is that until guns could be manufactured in series, each identical with the other, the development of gunnery as a science was more or less impossible. Any ballistic experiments carried out applied only to the weapon used for the actual test. The results had to be modified by empiric rule of thumb before they could be applied to any other gun. Thus in effect, it was the knowledge and skill of the individual gunner that governed the shooting in battle, and not an abstract set of range tables or mathematical theories.

GUNS

Any attempt to produce an exact classification of early eighteenth century artillery pieces is doomed to end in confusion, and the following remarks are but a generalisation. In all countries the actual weapons were basically similar, although nomenclature differed vastly. The Swedish King Gustavus Adolphus can justly be considered as the father of modern gunnery in that he made the first effort to

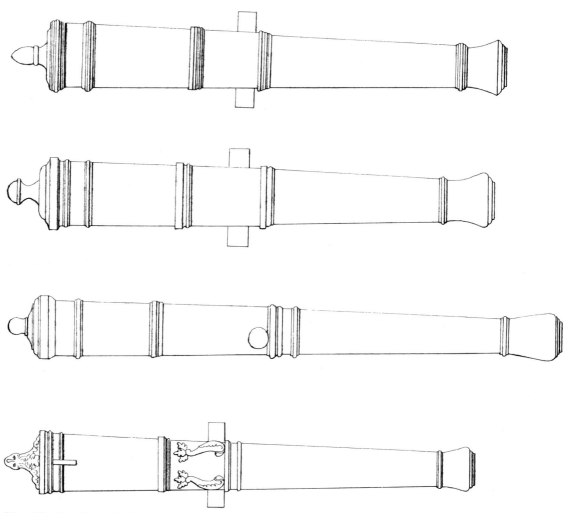

Fig. 50. Gun barrels. Top to **Bottom,** *Swedish iron 18 pounder, 1694. Spanish iron 24 pounder, circa 1720. English 'Rose and Crown' gun, 1710. French pattern of circa 1720.*

standardise the variety of calibres in use in his army. However, in 1700, some cannon were still being called by their Renaissance names, such as saker and minion, culverin and demi-cannon, while others exactly the same were graded according to the weight of shot they fired.

Basically, a cannon was either a field or siege weapon that employed direct fire against a visible target. Shot from it followed a fairly flat trajectory. Most were made of bronze, although some armies used iron pieces. Bronze was more expensive, but less liable to burst and thus the walls could be made thinner to produce a lighter and hence more mobile gun. Iron was cheaper,

but cracked easily when dropped and its useful life was only about 1,200 rounds.

The most important factor for classification of a cannon was its bore length, reckoned in calibres – a thirty calibre gun was thirty times the barrel diameter, measured from the muzzle to the touch-hole. In a book published in 1689,[3] Sir Jonas Moore defined an 'Ordinary' gun as thirty-two calibres, an 'Extraordinary' as being between thirty-nine and forty-one calibres, while a 'Bastard' was twenty-six to twenty-eight. A 'small' barrel was a comparatively thin one, a 'common' one was of normal thickness and 'reinforced' or 'fortified' meant a barrel with an extra thickness of metal.

The latter classifications could also be referred to as 'lesser', 'standard' and 'greater' respectively, which when translated into German or French gave roughly equivalent terms.

The siege guns, often referred to as 'cannons of battery', were generally short barrelled compared to field pieces, but with a larger bore. The heaviest in general use was the 'cannon' which fired shot weighing between 30 and 50 lbs, followed by the 'demi-cannon' from 20 to 28 lbs and the 'quarter-cannon' from 16 to 18 lbs.

The culverin was used both for siege and field work in its various sub-divisions, and the smaller and more portable field guns were the demi-culverins, sakers, minions and falcons. In an attempt to clarify the situation, the following table lists the principal types in use at the time, the information for which has been culled from a variety of sources. It is emphasised that the data are strictly of a general nature as no two sources are able to agree on such matters as range, etc.

Name(s)	Wt of shot fired in lbs	Point blank range in yds	Max. range in yds	Total wt in lbs
Heavy:				
Demi-cannon	24	600	6,000	5,500
Culverin	16	450	5,000	4,500
Medium:				
12 pdr,	12	450	4,000	2,000
Demi-culverin	9	400	2,400	2,000
Light:				
¼-culverin / Saker	5	360	2,200	1,500
Minion	4	350	2,000	800
½-Saker / Falcon	2	320	1,900	450
Falconet	1	300	1,800	200

With regard to the above, point blank range was defined as the distance travelled by a shot when fired from a gun without elevation or depression. Maximum range was the distance which a shot could be fired at maximum elevation (circa 45 deg.), but represented only an ideal figure. Obviously, the thicker the barrel wall, the greater the charge of powder that a gun would take, which thus influenced the range.

However, charges were small in comparison to the weight of shot, and with the inherent windage muzzle velocities were small. The shot could be seen in flight and in contemporary accounts there are many references to men being able to dodge a cannon ball. In practical terms, the effective range of a gun was little more than point blank, as after that the speed of the ball diminished rapidly.

French guns of the period were in a state of transition and featured an additional classification – those of the 'old' and the 'new invention'. The old guns had been standardised in the 1690s to six calibres – the 'Spanish' 12 and 24 pdrs and the 'French' 33, 16, 8 and 4 pdrs, but all of these had roughly the same barrel length – roughly 11 feet. The reason for this was a simple one. Unlike comparable English pieces, the French guns were designed for use both in the field and in fixed fortifications. In the latter, the guns had to be able to fire from embrasures and to project beyond them – otherwise the muzzle flash and the shock wave of detonation would have damaged the embrasure walls. This meant that with a standard barrel length, the smaller guns were at a disadvantage in having far too long a barrel, and were thus too heavy.

A 'greater' French gun of the 'old' system was designed to take a powder charge equivalent to the weight of the ball to be fired, a 'standard', four-fifths, and a 'lesser', two-thirds.

In an effort to overcome this problem, various experiments were carried out, culminating in the guns of the 'new invention' which featured a redesigned chamber. This improved pattern permitted a far smaller powder charge to be used to achieve the same results and thus the new guns could be cast with substantially less metal – reductions in weight up to a half could be achieved with consequent improvements in mobility.

In spite of all the above detail, guns in Europe looked remarkably similar in shape and design. Trunnions were cast on at the point of balance to attach the barrel to the carriage and to allow it to pivot. The touch-hole was on top

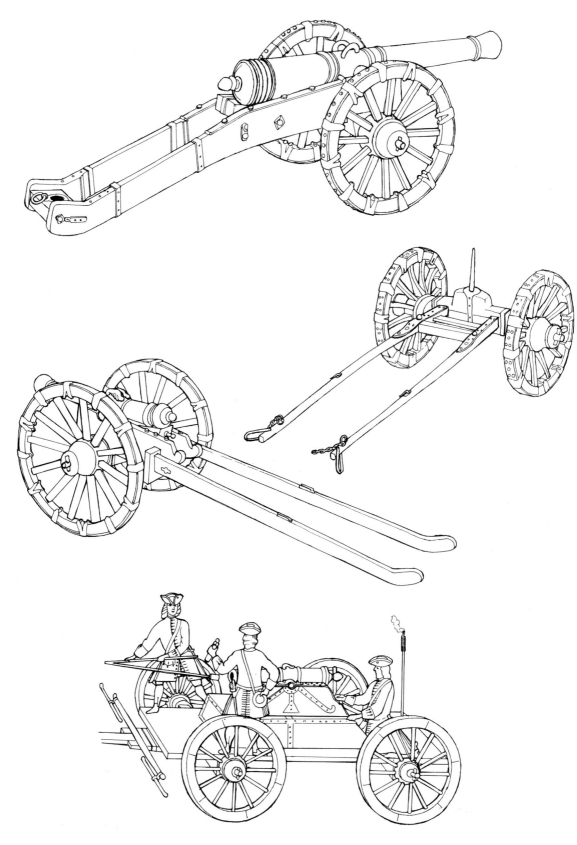

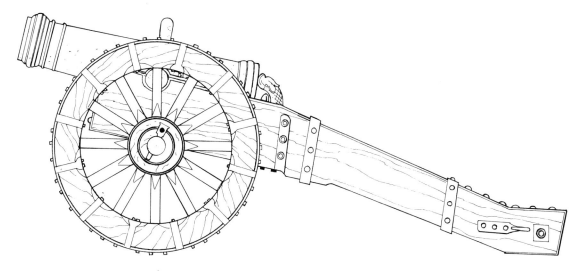

Fig. 52. Above *a French siege carriage, Louis XIV period. A short stubby gun mounted in a massive wooden cradle.*

Fig. 51. Left *gun carriages.* Top, *English field gun and limber.* Centre, *English 'galloper' carriage for a light gun.* Bottom, *Hanoverian regimental piece on a mobile carriage (from* Nec Aspera Terrent).

directly over the chamber. For hoisting the barrel on and off its carriage, dolphins were fitted on top also at the point of balance – two simple lugs would have sufficed but the dolphin was a traditional motive. Decoration of the barrel itself could be extremely ornate in keeping with Baroque tastes. The English guns were comparatively sober with the embossed or engraved royal arms (often of the Tudor Rose and Crown pattern), the name of the manufacturer and the date. Continental guns were often a riot of scrollwork and with such fancies as the muzzle aperture cast to represent the mouth of a lion or other beast. French guns carried the royal arms and motto plus the arms of the Duc de Maine who was *Maître-Général* of the Ordnance. Besides being a weapon of war, the gun was a symbol of the power and sovereignty of its owner, which had to be graphically expressed.

So far we have been referring to single barrel weapons. As in the case of hand-guns, however, inventors turned their attention to ways of increasing the rate of fire by means of multi-barrel guns. The French had a number of three barrel guns each of which was a 4-poun-

der of roughly 3 inch calibre. The barrels were arranged in a triangular pattern within a solid bronze casting, but all three touch-holes were on top. Each could be fired individually or, by laying a trail of powder across all three vents, the barrels could be discharged at once.[4]

A number of these 'secret-weapons' were captured by the Allies and two of them are preserved in the Rotunda Museum at Woolwich on replica carriages. These two are stated to have been taken at Malplaquet.

CARRIAGES

Essentially, all guns were mounted on two-wheel wooden carriages of roughly similar design, regardless of the size of the barrel. The purpose of the carriage was to enable the gun to be moved along the roads and into action. The basic parts were the two sides of the trail, known as cheeks, which were baulks of timber approximately the thickness of the calibre of the gun they were designed to support. These were joined by the axle beam and a varying number of wooden transoms. Between them the gun

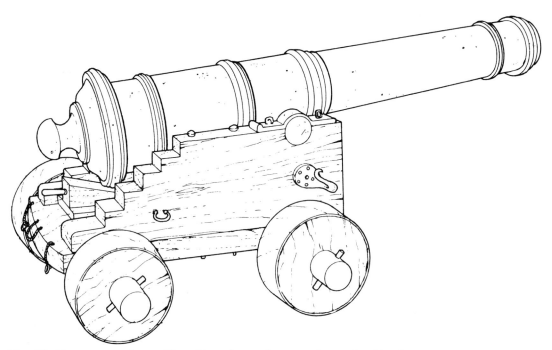

Fig. 53. Fortress carriages. Top, *French garrison carriage after Vauban*. Bottom, *the naval truck type carriage, popular in England and in France for coast artillery.*

could be elevated or depressed as it pivoted on its trunnions which were held in place by iron caps. Although the elevating screw had been discovered, the barrel was still usually raised or lowered by means of wedges jammed underneath the breech end.

The large spoked wheels were iron shod, and the tyres were held in place on the rims either by large nails or by iron tie bands which passed round both tyre and rim. The ends of the trail were also iron shod.

To move the gun from place to place, a limber

was required. This consisted of two road wheels joined by an axle beam and fitted with a pair of shafts for the first horse of the team to be hitched. In the centre of the axle beam was an upright post which fitted into a hole bored through the transom separating the two ends of the trail. To move off, the limber was man-handled into position, the rear of the trail was lifted over and dropped on to the post, and the team was hitched up.

Another type of field carriage that made its appearance during the early part of the eight-eenth century was the so-called Galloper. This was designed to support small guns of 3-poun-der size and below in order to give them mobi-lity on the battlefield. The axle was wider than in the normal carriage so that the trail cheeks could be spread more widely apart. This early form of 'split trail' could then be used for har-nessing a single horse or for enabling a crew of men to easily move the gun. On either side of the barrel were small chests in which a ready-use store of ammunition could be carried, as well as the necessary tools.

For use in fortresses, as mobility was not required, special types of carriages were used and a lower profile for the gun was necessary. The standard pattern was the garrison car-riage, which was basically similar to the naval truck carriage used on board warships. Stepped wooden cheeks supported the gun on its trun-nions and the whole issue could move back-wards and forwards on its four small wheels. On either side of the embrasure were heavy iron rings through which blocks and tackles could be fixed to haul the gun forward after it had been loaded. A French type of fortress carriage developed by Vauban dispensed with the rear wheels, elongating the sides of the truck to form a stubby trail.

The basic problem inherent in any carriage design of the period was that it had to withstand the shock of detonation and be able to absorb the full weight of the recoil – which was trans-mitted down the trail sides and into the ground. On muddy surfaces this could be a problem as the trail would dig itself firmly in. For static batteries during a siege, the heavy guns were stood on secure wooden platforms, but in the field this was impossible. After every round, the guns had to be levered forward with hand-spikes and muscle power.

In the absence of any mechanical means of absorbing recoil, carriages had to be extremely robust and thus heavy. Looking at period illus-trations, there seems to have been little concept of such matters as weight distribution or elegance. Very often, small guns were placed on large bulky carriages and vice versa. Friction on the hubs and the limber post was overcome with liberal applications of various substances – sope [sic] and tallow were common, and Uncle Toby refers to something mysterious called 'train grease'.[5]

Thinking of the roads along which the guns travelled, and the wear and tear in the field, breakages must have been frequent. St Rémy specified a spare carriage which accompanied each detachment on the march, and the artisans with the train must have been kept very busy in effecting running repairs.

AMMUNITION

The basic powder of the charge was so-called black powder of a somewhat coarser grain than used in muskets and other hand firearms. This caused rapid barrel encrustation and clouds of dense greyish-white smoke. On a still day, a battery would have been enveloped after a few rounds, making it impossible to observe the fall of their shot. Powder was composed of varying proportions of saltpetre, charcoal and sulphur, and opinions differed as to the exact quantities. As a guide, the proportions were roughly 75, 15 and 10 parts respectively. However, qualities of powder arriving at the guns could differ by up to 20 per cent in concentration, making any attempt at range computing a somewhat inexact business.[6]

Bulk powder was transported in barrels each holding 100 pounds, but transport over a dis-tance on bumpy roads could cause its ingredi-ents to settle and separate, besides which it was

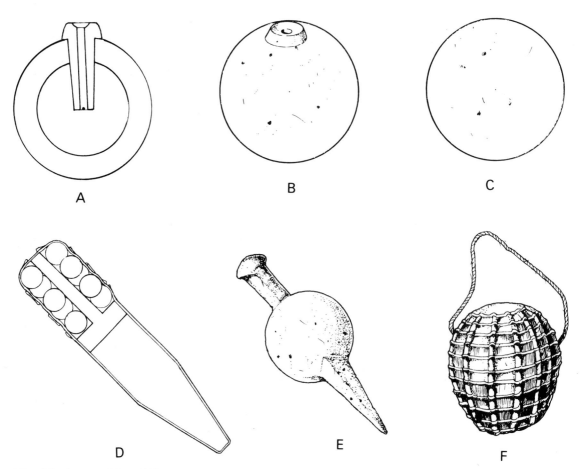

Fig. 54. Ammunition. (A) cross-section of a hollow shell. (B) shell exterior. (C) common shot. (D) canister or case shot with bagged charge. (E) spike shot. (F) a carcass incendiary.

naturally vulnerable to damp. Therefore, when the gunner opened a fresh barrel he was never quite sure what it would be like.

To load a gun, the most common method was to ladle the powder direct from the large container or to use a small, more portable item known as a budge barrel. To avoid dangerous leakage, the actual powder was packed inside its barrel in a cloth bag which could be closed at the top by a drawstring to keep out sparks. Some types of budge barrel had a hinged flap as a lid. Although commonly referred to as a ladle, the loading device was more in the form of a scoop on a long handle. The top was open so that the gunner took it full of powder, thrust it down the barrel into the chamber and then turned it over to empty it.

Popular with the French artillery was the cloth cartridge, although St Rémy suggested the use of parchment as it would burn better. Such cartridges could be made up in bulk in advance and their contents could be accurately weighed, thus ensuring equality from round to round. They could be filled with differing amounts from between two-thirds and half the weight of the shot to be fired, thus giving the gunner various options.

When loaded, the cartridge had to be pricked by poking through the touch-hole with a large needle in order to prime it. An alternative method was to force a powder filled tube through the touch-hole with enough force to penetrate the bag.

The normal projectile fired by all types of gun was the solid iron roundshot. Like a musket ball these had to have sufficient windage to fit into an encrusted bore. Too tight a fit would have resulted in excessive recoil, thus damaging the carriage, and if a shot became jammed in the bore, a burst gun would have been the result. A good artilleryman was equipped with a pair of calipers or a set of rings through which he passed the shot before loading, to check its diameter – very useful when firing captured ammunition.

A variant employed in siege warfare was to fire red-hot shot with the aim of setting fire to the buildings inside a fortress – a form of eighteenth-century 'frightfulness'. This was also popular at sea for setting fire to the sails and rigging of wooden ships.

The simplest way of heating shot in the field was to dig a pit and fill it with charcoal. When the fire was hot enough, an iron grid was placed over the top and loaded with iron shot. The gun was then loaded with its charge and raised to a high angle of elevation so that the projectile would drop on to the target from above. Next, a wad of turf or dampened hay was placed in the bore to keep the glowing shot away from the charge. When all was ready, a shot was fished out of the fire with a pair of large iron tongs, rushed to the gun and dropped down the bore. It was best then to fire the piece as quickly as possible before it had a chance to burn through the wad.

The other type of ammunition fired by field guns was case-shot in its various forms, known collectively to the English as 'partridge'. The two basic types were grape and canister. Grape consisted of a number of small iron balls clustered around a wooden core and held in place by cord or metal straps. Canister as its name implied was a wooden, fabric or tin container full of small shot. Both types burst open when they left the muzzle and scattered their projectiles over a wide area. Their use was restricted to short-range anti-personnel work, and both grape and canister were fired extensively on the battlefield by the infantry support guns.

A final variant was the spiked shot. This was a round shot with an integrally cast spike sticking out of one side. It was wrapped with an incendiary substance which was lit by the flash of the discharge, and used like red-hot shot for firing against wooden buildings – in the hope that the spike would arrive end-on and embed itself.

MORTARS

Developed from the earliest vase shape guns, mortars were a high-angle weapon used exclusively for siege work. Various types were in use in the early eighteenth century and they came in a vast number of different sizes. Some fired at a fixed elevation of 45 degrees and thus their range could only be adjusted by altering the amount of the powder charge. Of the adjustable types, some had trunnions at the point of balance while others had trunnions at the base. Mortars were mounted on sturdy wooden beds on to which they were clamped by metal caps fitting over the trunnions. Where possible, the angle of elevation was changed by using wooden wedges.

As they were not mobile, they had to be hoisted from their carrying carts and into position. The barrels often had cast dolphins or lugs for this purpose, while the beds were fitted with projecting metal bars on either side or metal rings. The really heavy mortars required a sheerlegs before they could be positioned.

The smallest mortars were the Coehoorns, named after Baron Menno van Coehoorn, Dutch military engineer and field general during the War of the Spanish Succession. These were anti-personnel weapons that could fire small bombs or even hand-grenades. Identical in construction to their larger counterparts, they could be carried by two men who simply took hold of lugs or handles fixed to the bed. Calibres ranged from $2\frac{1}{4}$ to $4\frac{1}{2}$ inches. When fired they tended to leap into the air, which meant constant repositioning, but they were apparently reasonably accurate up to about 150 yards.

The main siege mortars went up to 18 inches in calibre, but those generally used ranged be-

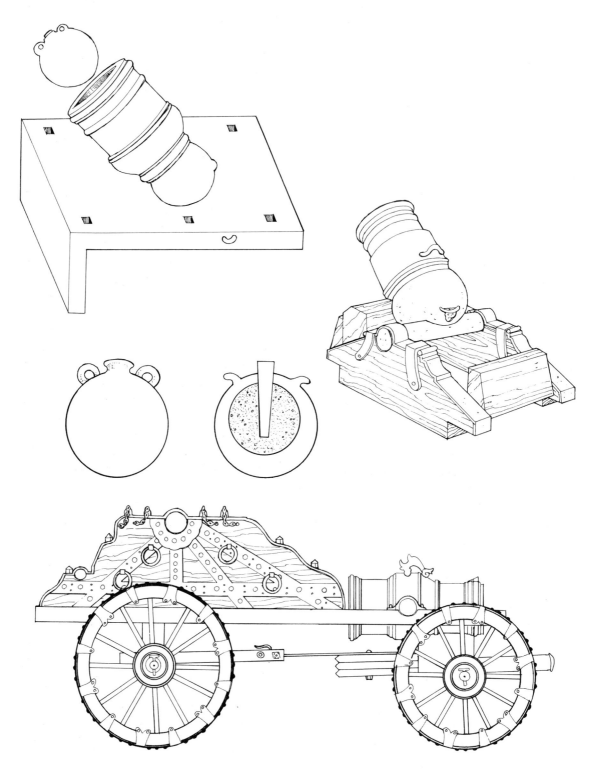

Fig. 55. Mortars. Top, *a French naval mortar, circa 1690.* Centre, *French siege mortar and bed, circa 1700, plus types of bomb.* Bottom, *a Dutch howitzer showing method of transportation.*

tween 8 and 13 inches. Essentially they were comparatively thin walled and were designed as chambered pieces – i.e. the chamber was smaller in diameter than the bore. St Rémy gives four standard sizes in French service at the end of the seventeenth century – 18, $12\frac{1}{2}$, $8\frac{1}{3}$ and $6\frac{1}{4}$ inches.[7] As a general guide, an English 13 inch mortar weighed some two tons, but the equivalent French ones were lighter, having a shorter barrel in relation to the calibre. All were made of bronze.'

The basic ammunition fired by mortars was the hollow shell filled with explosive, known at the time as a bomb. These were iron globes, cast slightly thicker at the base than at the top in the pious hope that the infernal machine would thus land the right way up and not stifle the fuze in an inconvenient patch of mud.

A wooden tube was inserted into the hole at the top to form a fuze holder. This was cone-shaped and long enough to reach to the bottom of the bomb. Through its centre a quarter inch diameter hole was drilled which was filled with slow-burning powder. In theory, when lit, the powder flamed to the bottom of the tube in the time which the bomb took to travel when fired at maximum elevation and maximum propelling charge. For lesser ranges and charges, a given amount could be cut from the end of the fuze before it was inserted.

The bombs were filled in advance and the fuzes were stored separately, sealed with covers of pitch or wax. To load them into the mortars, the larger calibres had two carrying lugs on either side of the fuze holder.

An alternative filling sometimes used was plain sand. De la Colonie mentions this form of deception in connection with the siege of Charleroi in 1693 when a party of grenadiers were ordered to storm a half-moon work in the fortifications. They were ordered to advance when 'twelve small mortars would be fired together into the half-moon battery, the third time the shells would be loaded with sand only, with long fuzes, so as to keep the besieged lying flat as long as possible in expectation of the explosions.'[8]

Another type of mortar projectile was the carcass which was essentially an incendiary device used against inflammable buildings inside a fortress. Deane, commenting on the siege of Lille in 1708, wrote: 'For what was not killed or wounded were spoiled by their hellish inventions of throwing of bombs, boiling pitch, tar, oil and brimstone with scalding water and such like combustibles from the outworks and when our men made any attack.' He was referring here to somewhat mediaeval methods of defending a fortress, but combustibles were also popular in attack. The carcass was supposedly invented by the bishop of Münster, obviously a staunch representative of the church militant.[9] They were formed from a metal cap and a framework of iron bands. The interior was then filled with a sticky mixture of melted pitch and gunpowder, and as an added refinement small grenades could be embedded in the mass. The carcass was touched off by the flash of the charge and landed as a flaming explosive mass in the middle of the town. A different type was made by taking a normal powder filled mortar bomb, smaller than the calibre of weapon that was to fire it, and coating the outside with the combustible mass. This then exploded on arrival, flinging the burning material in all directions.

They even had flares in those days. Returning to de la Colonie at the siege of Charleroi, he mentions that the siege works were discovered by the enemy who showered his men with

'fire-pots in the same way as bombs would be thrown. A fire-pot is a kind of globe or large ball filled with old rope well tarred, which burns with a very bright light. This globe – set alight before being thrown – will burn for a considerable time, and lights up a wide area upon which cannon may be directed as effectively as if by the light of day. To prevent an attempt to extinguish it (in itself not an easy task, owing to the tar and composition therein) small pistol barrels are screwed into its surface, loaded with ball, which discharge themselves successively as the fire approaches them.'[10]

A final type of mortar was the *pierrier* or stone-throwing weapon. Stones were naturally cheaper than specially made iron projectiles, and just as hard. Baskets were filled with stones and loaded in the normal way into the larger mortars. On arrival at the target, they burst asunder scattering their load in all directions.

HOWITZERS

The name probably comes from the German *haubitze*. Essentially these were mobile mortars, being mounted on carriages similar to field guns, and were introduced by the Dutch in the seventeenth century. The best of the early eighteenth-century versions was the English 10 inch which could fire a shell at a range of some 1,200 yards. Just over three and a half feet long, the barrel weighed 1,500 lbs. Howitzers were mainly reserved for siege work, but they began to be used in the field for firing bombs against troop concentrations. A howitzer can be easily recognised by its short stubby barrel fitted between the cheeks of a standard trail carriage.

ARTILLERY OPERATION

So far we have discussed the pieces, their characteristics and the projectiles they were designed to fire. Now it is necessary to examine how the various types were actually operated in the field and the equipment required. One difficulty has been to discover any form of recognised gun drills. Contemporary pictures tend to show odd men grouped around a gun without any sense of order and items of equipment just lying around the place. Therefore the following descriptions are somewhat of a general nature.

The various calibres of siege and field gun were all operated along broadly similar lines. The crewmen required differed from country to country and depended often on the numbers of personnel available. Normally, an artillery piece would be served by a trained gunner and two or three 'matrosses' or assistants who belonged to the artillery train and had had some form of training. However, it was clear that more men were required as labourers to manhandle such heavy weapons, and these were mainly detached from the infantry. As already mentioned, the drivers and carters were civilians. Where separate fusilier or line infantry regiments were employed to guard the guns, they would probably have helped to operate them in battle or during a siege.

Each gun required a number of items of equipment to accompany it into action, and a specimen list is given below.

> Ramrod (ideally plus a spare).
> Sponge or mop on a pole.
> Worm on a pole, for scraping an encrusted bore.
> Wadhook, for removing the wad in case of a misfire.
> Powder ladle.
> Powder bucket or budge barrel.
> Water bucket.
> Wedges, for altering elevation.
> Wheel chocks.
> Touch-hole (vent) cover.
> Tompions (metal or wood muzzle plugs for keeping out rain).
> Handspikes (on average four) for levering the gun into position.

The above list represents an ideal, and not every gun would have had all of the items. It must also be emphasised that owing to non-standardisation, many items were not interchangeable, being individually suited to a particular gun.

The gunner himself needed a linstock, powder, flask for priming, his instruments (quadrant, shot calipers or rings, etc.) and a portfire in a holder.

In addition to the above, each gun would have been equipped with a number of drag ropes, lashing chains, etc., and a ready-use supply of ammunition easily available (see later section on tactics).

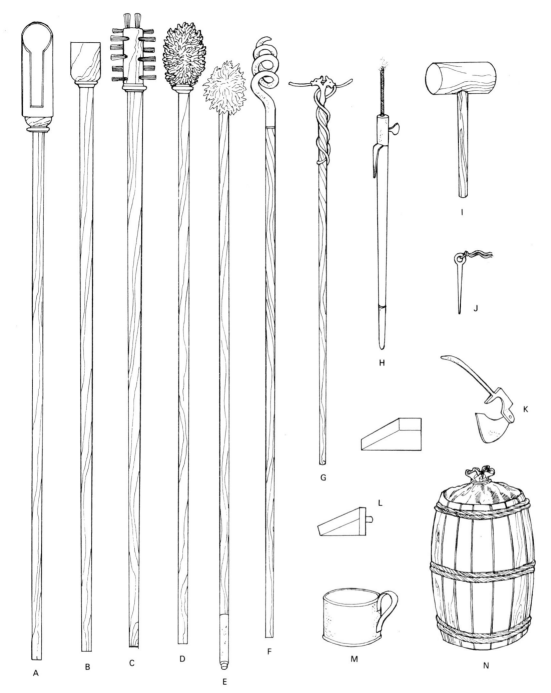

Fig. 56. (A) Ladle, (B) Rammer, (C) Scraper, (D) Mop, (E) Mop, (F) Worm, (G) Linstock, (H) Portfire, (I) Mallet in Holder, (J) Spike, (K) Portfire cutter, (L) Quoins, (M) Powder measure, (N) Powder barrel.

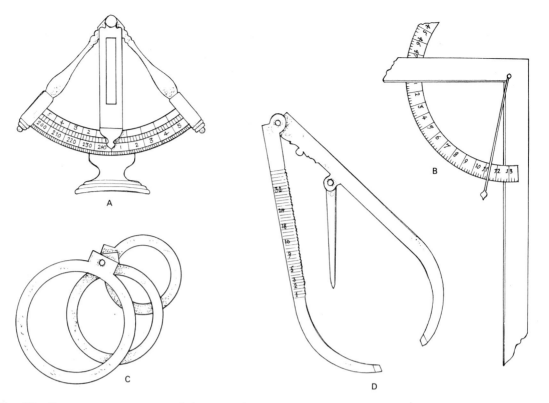

Fig. 57. Gunnery instruments. (A) gunner's level. (B) gunner's quadrant. (C) shot measuring rings. (D) shot calipers.

The basic method of operation was as follows, assuming that the gun was in its correct position. The gunner took his linstock, made sure that it was alight and glowing, and stuck it into the ground near the rear of the gun. A linstock was a pole, the top of which had a two-branched clamp to hold a length of slow-match. This type of match was a length of braided cotton or hemp which had been impregnated with saltpetre, causing it to burn slowly, leaving a glowing end. During a lengthy period of operations, vast quantities would have been required. The only figure that I could discover was of an earlier date during the siege of Lyme in the English Civil War. The garrison of 1,500 men used five hundredweight in 24 hours. Admittedly they were armed mainly with matchlock muskets, but they would not have had many guns, so perhaps a comparison could be made with the artillery available at a siege during the War of the Spanish Succession.[11]

One man then took the dry mop and swept the bore to remove any dirt, after which the powder ladle was filled from the budge barrel or sack and the charge was inserted, great care being taken that no traces of powder were spilled on the ground near the muzzle. A man at the rear then 'served the vent' by placing his finger over the touch-hole. The idea of this was to stop any powder being forced up through the vent while the gunner at the front operated the ramrod with two or three good strong strokes to neatly compress the charge.

The next stage was to insert the wad which was made of a number of materials – turf, plaited straw, rushes, etc. – and ram this home. If nothing better was available, earth or even dung was used. Finally, the ball was inserted, and if he was wise, the man doing this stood well to the side in case of an accidental discharge.

The gun being loaded, it then had to be aligned. It was manhandled forward by men heaving at the wheels and using handspikes as levers. For correct alignment, handspikes were placed under the trail which was then heaved to left or right as the gunner directed. Aiming was a more or less empiric procedure. Field guns in combat were normally fired at point blank range, and as no real sights were fitted they were simply pointed in the approximate direction of the enemy. Corrections could be applied by observing the fall of shot.

Over longer ranges, as with the larger siege guns, the gunners 'fired at random', which meant just that. In view of the variations in powder quality, the only way was to make a 'guesstimate' and see what would happen. There were a variety of range tables, but as these took no account of wind resistance, wind effect, etc., they were of little use. The normal method was to place one arm of the quadrant in the muzzle and read off the angle of elevation from a bob weight suspended from a piece of string which moved across a curved scale. Another device was the clinometer, which was stood on the barrel at the muzzle end and also gave an angle of elevation reading. Adjustments were then carried out by means of shifting the wedges under the breach in or out to raise or lower the muzzle.

To fire the gun, the gunner primed the touch-hole with powder from his flask and, taking the linstock, applied this, having first blown on the end to ensure a good glow. The pole of the linstock was about six feet long, as the man operating it had to be able to stand well clear to avoid the recoil. In the French army, an officer (*officier pointeur*) attached to each battery was responsible for aiming and actually firing each gun.

Once the first round was on its way, the loading process began all over again. Ideally, the barrel had to be swabbed out between each round with a mop dipped in a bucket of water to which some vinegar had been added. This was both to cool the barrel and to ensure that there were no glowing remains from the last charge. If this was not done and the next powder charge ignited prematurely, the poor man wielding the ramrod was likely to go for a trip still hanging on to it.

After some thirty rounds, the gun had to be scraped out with the worm to remove the encrusted ash deposits. Rates of fire are difficult to determine, but a fair average would be about 20 rounds per hour, with a well-trained crew managing perhaps 30. When used for an excessive amount of time as during a siege bombardment, the bronze cannon could start to melt, becoming so soft that the vent enlarged and the unsupported muzzles began to droop – in such a case the only answer was to saw off the front section of the barrel.

Before leaving the operation of guns, a word should be said about a different method of touching them off that appeared about this time. The linstock was retained, but the gunner had a so-called port-fire which was a length of quick-match clamped into a holder. He lit this from the main linstock and when he had fired his gun, he nipped off the burning end with a small cutter.

The gun drill illustrated is based on St Rémy and may be purely theoretical. He advocated two trained gunners and six assistants per piece, backed up by a further six men in reserve to replace casualties. The two gunners were responsible for collecting the powder and loading it. The three men on each side operated sponge and rammer, brought up wads and shot, and levered the gun into position.[12]

For mortars and howitzers, different factors applied. The vent was served and the charge was inserted with the ladle in the normal way. This was rammed, the wad inserted and rammed again to make doubly certain the chamber was entirely filled with powder. At this stage, elevation was checked and adjusted if required. With the muzzle pointing upwards, the bomb was brought and inserted into place, with the fuze pointing upwards. It was then centred in the bore by being packed with earth or straw. Carrying handles for two men had to be

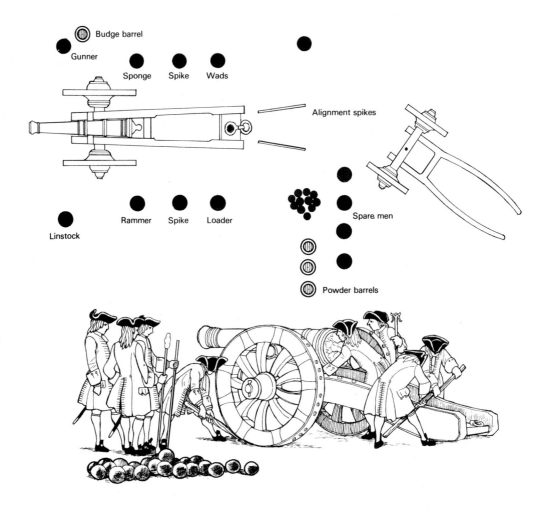

Fig. 58. Top, *typical artillery drill showing positions of crew.* Bottom, *French siege gun in action from a contemporary engraving.*

placed through the lugs of the heavier bombs.

Then came the dangerous part. The earlier method was to remove the protective cover from the fuze, upon which the gunner advanced with a piece of glowing slow-match in each hand. The trick was to touch off both bomb and touch-hole as quickly as possible and more or less simultaneously – and then stand well clear. If the main charge misfired, the bomb could well explode in the barrel with alarming results.

An improvement on this method was to use a double-branched linstock with which both bomb and charge were lit together. It was not until some time in the early eighteenth century

that automatic ignition for bombs was discovered. The English practice had been to load mortars without wads, and possibly as a result of fitting a bomb with fuze downwards by mistake it was found that the flash of the charge would light the fuze. This obviated the danger of misfire, as if the charge failed, the bomb remained safe. Thus a method was developed whereby the bomb was centred in the bore by means of wooden wedges directly on top of the rammed charge.

The man in charge of a mortar or howitzer crew was often entitled the 'fire-worker' in view of his involvement with explosive shells, and he had two or three assistants.

90

Safety was an ever-present problem, and although precautions were taken, the presence of fire and powder was an unstable environment. A closed lantern was available if the linstock went out, and naturally the glow of the linstock itself was an invitation to disaster. Powder barrels could leak and men could be careless, which was understandable in the heat of action. One of the worst crimes a member of a gun crew could commit was to leave the powder sack or budge barrel open between rounds. However, not far to the rear was the bulk powder supply which a chance shell could easily ignite. A gunner's life could be a short if merry one.

ARTILLERY ORGANISATION

Although perhaps not directly connected with the subject of this book, it is useful to have a working knowledge of the organisation behind those who actually operated the guns in action. In both France and England, and to a certain extent in other countries in Europe, the artillery authorities had developed parallel to the regular armies. This reflected royal determination to keep control of the manufacture and supply of guns in the days when armies were still simply mercenary bands.

In England the Board of Ordnance, under its Master-General, was responsible for the supply of artillery both to the army and the navy, the provision of engineering services, the training of gunners and the issue of a multitude of stores items, including small arms. It was a Department of State completely separate from the army and answerable only to the Treasury – its staff wore blue coats instead of red and usually received somewhat higher pay than their equivalents in the ranks. The permanent staff consisted of five Principal Officers and perhaps some 150 lesser luminaries, some of whom served in the field. Their jobs depended on the Master-General and they were not permitted to buy and sell their commissions.

When war broke out, the Board supplied the artillery train and most of its personnel, and the guns were only nominally controlled by the Commander-in-Chief.

The *Grand Maître* of artillery in France was an office dating from the early part of the sixteenth century, but as in other spheres of military activity, a new organisation was created under Louvois. As France was a much larger country, there was a considerable degree of decentralisation with a number of provincial artillery authorities responsible for manufacture and storage of guns and equipment.

The *Grand Maître* was a royal appointee, usually a Prince of the Blood, who controlled a considerable headquarters staff as well as the provincial bodies. Although the system was more complex than in England, it is probable that the Master-General had more actual power than his French counterpart, as in the latter country after 1703 commissions could be traded in. The *Corps Royal d'Artillerie* was the basic pool of trained personnel divided up among the various fortresses and garrisons and who would have served in the field during wartime. They were supplemented by the *Régiment Royal d'Artillerie* which was an all officer formation on which the provincial organisation was based, companies of miners and the *Régiment des Bombardiers*, initially an infantry unit to guard the guns. All these various groups were brought in 1721, together with the artillery schools, into a comprehensive artillery formation.

By contrast, as a result of the Board's unpreparedness when the Jacobite rebellion broke out in 1715, the following year saw the foundation on a regular basis of the Royal Regiment of Artillery in England.

The sprawling Hapsburg Empire also had a decentralised set-up with a headquarters under the *Feldseckhmeister* and a number of provincial authorities under ranking generals, each with their own staffs. The smaller German armies naturally had fewer guns and their artillery organisations were normally of regimental size. The Dutch had a system similar to the English under the command of the *Meester-General*.

All the above organisations reflected to a certain extent the traditionally specialist nature of artillerymen and their origins as craftsmen rather than gentleman soldiers. Gunners tended to remain a separate caste, although in the course of the eighteenth century they became more and more absorbed into their respective armies.

In the field, artillery was organised into trains, which also included the engineers, pioneers and pontoons. In English service, the basic problem until the establishment of the Royal Regiment in 1716 was impermanence – when peace was signed, the field organisation of the trains was broken up. Under William III, the artillery in Flanders had for the first time been divided up into companies to form an *ad hoc* regiment. However, at the Peace of Ryswick in 1697, the guns returned to the Tower, the infantry personnel returned to their regiments and the civilians went back to their peacetime posts. Only four under-strength companies were retained, together with a nucleus of experienced officers.[13]

The basis for the artillery used during Marlborough's campaigns was the Warrant for Holland of March, 1702, by which the Board of Ordnance was required to furnish fourteen sakers, sixteen 3-pounders and four howitzers. These comparatively small numbers were reinforced from time to time until a total of around forty-five was reached. This may not seem many, but was only the field artillery component. As a comparison, the total Allied guns at Blenheim were sixty, against ninety fielded by the Franco-Bavarian armies.

The actual guns of a train, however, were only the tip of the iceberg. Behind them and included in the train were the engineers and their stores, the bridging pontoons, the artillery stores, including all the necessary equipment for the supply of small-arms ammunition, and the only specialist tradesmen attached to the army.

An English train was normally commanded by a colonel who could well be an army officer, and under him he had a staff which was considerably larger than that of an infantry regiment. An important figure was the Comptroller, a Board of Ordnance employee who supervised the issues and receipts, and there were the usual officers – lieutenant-colonel and major. Then came the adjutant who dealt with the military side of administration, chaplain, quartermaster, provost-marshal, waggon-master, paymaster, etc. Many of the above were entitled to clerks, and the staff was completed by the kettle drummer and his 'coachman' (see section on military music).

The guns and their crews were divided up into companies, according to weapon sizes and types. Each was commanded by a captain assisted by 'Gentlemen of the Ordnance' and lieutenants. Among the lower orders there is some confusion – sergeants and corporals as well as gunners and matrosses are mentioned in sources. In addition, the howitzers and mortars had their complement of fireworkers.

The engineers and pioneers will be dealt with in the following chapter together with various matters concerning the siege as opposed to the field train. The latter, however, had a complicated infrastructure of skilled tradesmen and the inevitable storemen, clerks and Commissaries of Stores. The tradesmen – smiths, carpenters, wheelwrights, armourers, etc. – had to be able from the resources they carried with them, to repair almost everything – broken carriages and limbers, shattered waggon wheels, worn-out muskets, torn tents. As none of the cavalry regiments had a smith or farrier on the establishment, it is possible that the train specialists may have had to shoe horses for all comers.

All this polyglot collection formed a vast waggon train that followed the guns of every army. The basic waggon was a four-wheel open cart drawn by four or more horses harnessed sometimes in pairs and sometimes nose to tail. In addition there were the special vehicles such as field forges. These were basically a large portable bellows designed to be operated by hand and blowing on to a hearth fixed to the back of the cart. Another special waggon trans-

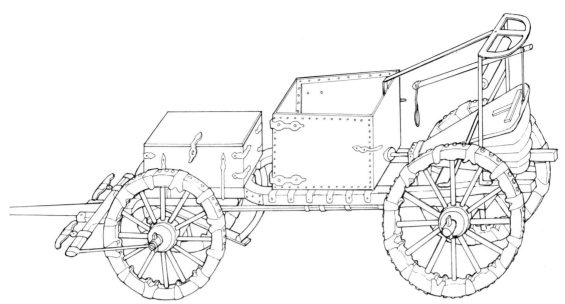

Fig. 59. Swedish field forge, circa 1700. The bellows operated directly into the fire box. Tools were in the forward chest.

ported the heavy sheer-legs required for shipping and unshipping gun barrels.[14]

For a typical French train of fifty guns for an army of 50,000 men we have to turn again to St Rémy.[15] He divided his train into five brigades, each of which was responsible for ten guns under the command of a senior captain, and the fifth brigade had additional responsibility for the specialists, pontoons, extra stores, etc.

One brigade of ten 8-pounders had twelve officers and staff plus some 60 gunners, assistants and civilian drivers. The actual guns were to be accompanied by a spare carriage, twenty two-wheel carts and a total of 144 horses. The whole train would have required for the fifty guns a grand total of 1,225 horses to pull them, plus 220 waggons for the stores and equipment.

Actual quantities of stores carried are naturally difficult to determine, as each army placed a different interpretation on what was necessary for a campaign. When moving in the fairly confined area of Flanders with its ample water communications, bulk stores could be left in the magazines at the rear and be sent out in convoys to replenish the trains as required.

Writing on a theoretical basis, St Rémy

reckoned that 100 rounds per gun for his train was sufficient ammunition to have readily available, and fifty rounds per gun should be transported by each brigade, together with 1,000 lbs of powder. As a comparison, each shot required roughly two-thirds its weight in powder – each 12 lb-ball needed 8 lbs of powder to fire it, so 100 rounds meant 800 lbs of powder.

Another coefficient is St Rémy's factor of 1 lb of powder per man per day of action, which was sufficient for the twenty-four shots which each musketeer was issued with, and 1 lb of ball (French muskets fired twenty-four to the pound).

Taking then his theoretical army of 50,000 and ignoring for the moment the cavalry, let us assume that we have an infantry component of 30,000. For a day of action they would require 30,000 lbs of powder and 30,000 lbs of lead ball. Add in fifty guns at an *average* calibre of 8-pounders each to fire fifty rounds, and we require a further 20,000 lbs of iron shot and 15,000 lbs of powder.

At 100 lbs of powder per barrel this would mean 450 containers to be transported. The French carried an average weight of 1,200 lbs

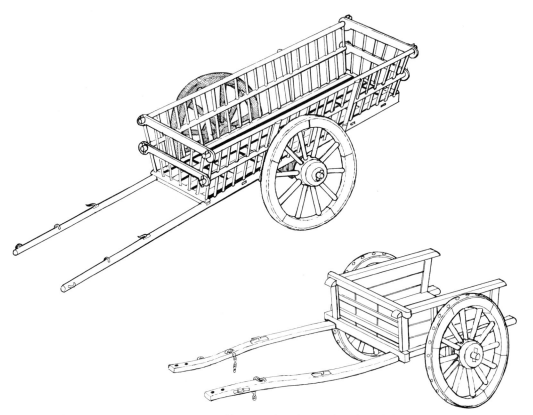

Fig. 60. Two-wheeled carts. Top, 'Charette à la manére de M. de Vigny' *(after St Rémy).* Bottom, *tumbril known as a 'marlbrouk' on the Continent.*

per cart, so the powder alone would have required forty carts, plus twenty-five carts for ball and seventeen for the shot.

One can go on playing with such statistics *ad infinitum*, and further details are given in the chapter concerned with armies on the march. The above figures are a very rough guide and do not take into account such items as grenades (1,000 per cart, packed in barrels), fuzes, matches, spare parts (ramrods, handspikes, etc.) and tools. We know comparatively little about the internal day-to-day organisation of the trains, but the various procedures, paperwork, etc., must have been fairly complex. What emerges is that the trains functioned fairly well within the limitations of poor roads – the guns arrived at the various battles in time to play their allotted part and the ammunition supply system seems to have functioned. This means that the personnel involved in the various armies were conscientious and tolerably well trained for their specialist role. The gunners may have started off as social pariahs, but by the beginning of the eighteenth century they were an indispensable part of any army. As they were organised on a more formal basis into regular regiments, they began to develop that pride and *esprit de corps*, ceasing to be a race apart who handled infernal substances, and became soldiers.

THE TACTICAL EMPLOYMENT OF ARTILLERY

The whole question of the movement of the artillery trains will be considered in a later chapter. The aim of such movement was to get the guns, their ammunition and stores, and their crews on to the battlefield at the right time and in the right place. Siege guns will feature in the next chapter, so here we are purely concerned with field artillery.

94

As the army approached the enemy with a view to giving battle, the senior officers would be up ahead with the main staff to select the positions for their batteries, while their subordinates toiled to bring forward the guns. With the type of two-line formation favoured at the time, the classic position for the artillery was to form up on both wings – so as to be able to fire into the flank of any enemy attack. However, during the War of the Spanish Succession, the tendency was for the guns to be formed up along and slightly in advance of the front line – the heavier ones in the centre and the lighter ones on the flanks. In addition, the English, Dutch and some German armies used small guns (3-pounders and below) as so-called regimental pieces, issued to the tune of two per battalion.

During a battle, the artillery was called upon to perform a variety of tasks, both offensive and defensive. If the guns could be brought on to the field in good time, they could be used to cover the assembly of the army as a whole, and many battles opened with a mutual cannonade. Once combat had been joined, the guns could defend threatened portions of the long and thus vulnerable battle line and, formed into batteries, could bombard such positions as field fortifications and defended villages. In a retreat, skilfully handled guns could help cover a withdrawal or give time for shattered formations to reform.

The basic problem was again the lack of mobility. The regimental pieces could be manhandled in an emergency, but a beaten army frequently lost the bulk of its artillery. The civilian drivers were notorious for their habit of running away (who can blame them?) and the recovery of guns called for swift team-work. If the enemy advanced, the guns had to be brought back into shelter behind the front line – which meant getting hold of the limber and the teams of horses.

If one's own side were advancing, they often had to leave their artillery support behind unless the ground was particularly suitable. One of the greatest feats was when Colonel Blood managed to get some guns across the marshy Nebel stream at Blenheim to support the threatened battalions commanded by the Duke of Holstein-Beck.

We have seen that in action, the guns seldom fired at more than point blank range. Round-shot was used for counter-battery work and to try to break up enemy formations at ranges of up to 600 yards. Partridge shot was fired into the close-packed ranks at short range by the smaller pieces. Where howitzers were used on the battlefield, they were set to fire their bombs to drop down on the enemy and explode among them. A skilled fireworker who could adjust his fuzes accordingly was capable of producing airbursts to unsettle the opposing cavalry. One way of extending the range of roundshot was to employ ricochet fire when the ground was firm enough. Like a stone skimming over water, the shot would bounce off the earth and slice in among the unfortunate soldiers causing them to scatter.

Once the respective positions had been determined, each gun moved up on its limber dragged by its team, and accompanied by its crew of fusiliers or detached infantry. It was then unlimbered and the ammunition supply was unloaded (thirty to fifty rounds per gun together with the necessary powder in barrels or pre-packed cartridges). Thus at least one waggon per gun must have accompanied them into the front line.

The teams, waggons and limbers would then withdraw to a position between the two battle lines where a replacement supply of ammunition would be held ready for issue if required, again guarded by fusiliers or infantry. The rest of the train with its bulk supplies of infantry and artillery ammunition and stores would form up somewhere behind the army, together with the baggage trains, to form the *grand parc*. I have not been able to discover any details of carrying parties for spare ammunition and supplies, but such a system must have existed.

Contemporary pictures show men rolling powder barrels along the ground from dumps to the rear of the guns, and in pairs, transporting cannon balls on sled-like affairs. The more permanent siege batteries had their magazines

Fig. 61. Artillery on the march (after St Rémy). Note how the limber was placed under the trail.

Fig. 62. Painting of the Battle of the Boyne by J. de Wyck. This detail shows a gun battery in action and the somewhat casual way in which equipment was littered about.

built into pits and roofed over with several layers of earth and turf. The basic problem was that the more powder you had in close proximity to the guns, the greater the danger of an accidental explosion. However, this could not be avoided unless one could devise a complicated system of carrying parties – which could easily break down under combat conditions.

It is clear that Marlborough himself was very interested in the siting of his artillery, and as Master-General of the Ordnance as well as being Captain-General, he provided a useful link between the army as a whole and the semi-civilian artillery command. The use of the guns in each battle was different, and a study of this is beyond the scope of this book. The guns, however, were effective and certainly caused casualties. During the bombardment prior to the engagement at Blenheim, the infantry were ordered to lie down to minimise the danger.

As the eighteenth century progressed, attention was paid to standardisation of calibres within a given army, and great strides were made in improving the techniques of gun-founding. Mobility became the key with the creation of the first horse artillery units. However, in tactical employment and organisation, little really changed until the middle of the nineteenth century.

NOTES

1 Atkinson. 12.

2 See Hall, *Ballistics in the 17th Century*, for a concise account of gun manufacture and the scientific status of gunnery.

3 Moore, Sir Jonas. *Modern Fortification, or Elements of Military Architecture*. London. 1689.

4 Blackmore. *The Armouries of the Tower of London*. Vol. i, 117–8.

5 Sterne. *Tristram Shandy*.

6 Hall. 55.

7 St Rémy. Vol. i, 217.

8 Colonie. 31.

9 Duffy. 99.

10 Colonie. 30.

11 Firth. *Cromwell's Army*. London. 1902. 83.

12 St Rémy. Vol. i, 101–3.

13 Fortescue. Vol. i, 343.

14 At the Rotunda Museum in Woolwich there is an interesting collection of models of Marlborough's artillery train.

15 St Rémy. Vol. ii, 229–30.

Fig. 63. An idealised representation of a siege battery by St Rémy. Note the well-protected powder magazine at the rear.

Fig. 64. St Rémy's mortar battery. The bombs were stored and filled at the rear. As they fired upwards, the mortars could be well hidden behind a high parapet.

ENGINEERING
AND SIEGES[1]

When studying seventeenth- and eighteenth-century warfare, one cannot help but be aware of the relatively high number of sieges compared to major land battles (25 : 9 in the War of the Spanish Succession). In fact, siege warfare proved attractive to many army commanders, especially those of a more timid nature. In those days, armies represented an enormous investment on the part of a monarch or state and the outcome of any battle was always a risky affair. Therefore it was preferable to engage in a number of sieges per campaign in order to improve one's position for the following year and to obtain bargaining counters for an eventual peace negotiation. In his lucid summary of the aims and objectives of eighteenth-century warfare, Michael Howard writes:

'To pile up such minor successes until their aggregated weight and financial exhaustion compelled the adversary to make peace seemed preferable to staking all on a battle in which advantages accumulated over several years might be thrown away in as many hours; especially since the political objectives for which the wars were fought were seldom such as to justify such bloody solutions'.[2]

The capture of a major fortress brought just as much international prestige as a victorious battle at far less cost. Louis XIV was very fond of sieges, as he could attend in person with his full court. They camped out in great splendour, treating the whole affair as an elaborate Baroque game which the King had to win.

From the above it should follow that the engineers of any Baroque army would have enjoyed high status and have been represented in large numbers. The fact is that the opposite was the case. The late seventeenth century produced two great engineers, the Frenchman Sebastian le Prestre de Vauban, who rose to become a Marshal of France, and the Dutchman Menno van Coehoorn. Apart from these luminaries, however, the engineers in most armies were often unjustly regarded as second-class soldiers of somewhat dubious quality. Frederick the Great was of the opinion that military engineering was a suitable occupation for the bourgeois officers who were unsuitable for a field command.

THE ENGINEERS

Like their counterparts in the artillery, professional military engineers in English service suffered from semi-civilian status – most of them were employees of the Board of Ordnance although the number was small. Under the Master-General was an official with the title of Surveyor-General who was responsible for everything pertaining to military engineering — which in practice meant that he was largely concerned with the coastal fortresses at home and in the colonies. Under him were three full-time engineers who might or might not have been soldiers, and a varying number of sub-engineers, clerks, storemen, etc., to form the nucleus of a headquarters.

This in itself is hardly surprising, as being an island, England has been spared the fate of continental countries where so many fine towns were turned into fortresses in the seventeenth and eighteenth centuries.

In the field, the engineers suffered from impermanence in that they were generally appointed for a specific campaign, and in fact many of them were seconded from infantry regiments. It was generally agreed that they had officer status but they did not necessarily enjoy military rank. The lucky ones were those who were able to retain their infantry commissions and thus pocket the pay and prerequisites.[3]

Colonie spent some of his time in Bavarian service as an engineer, as his employer, the Elector 'found himself embarrassed by his want of engineers, a want which had not been foreseen. There certainly were two or three officers with us who acted as engineers, but they were good for nothing that required originality'.[4]

The trains formed for the wars of William III normally contained five or six engineers, and Marlborough had roughly the same number. Under them they had companies of miners, pioneers and bridging personnel plus a few tradesmen. The vast labour forces required for extensive engineering operations were provided by drafts from the field army and the large scale hiring or impressment of civilians.

The quality of English engineers seems to have been varied and complaints abounded. If one reads the reports of the dilapidation of our coastal forts one cannot but conclude that the permanent staff of the Board were singularly incompetent, but much of the trouble lay in Parliamentary unwillingness to grant money. In 1704, Galway wrote from Spain: 'It is no easy thing to find good engineers, and a commission from the Board of Ordnance is not sufficient to make one . . . good engineers are so scarce, that one must bear with their humours and forgive them because we can't be without them.'[5]

Probably as a result of his experiences in the field, Marlborough initiated the first tentative steps towards creating a full-time professional service — along with the reformation of the artillery already referred to. As Master-General he submitted proposals for a permanent establishment which was finally approved in 1717, thus creating the nucleus of what was to become the Royal Engineers.

In view of their long history of having to both build and reduce fortifications, the French organisation was far more complex — greatly stimulated by Louis XIV's wars of conquest. His ill-gotten gains had to be fortified as quickly as possible to place them in a state of defence.

Under Vauban as *directeur général* the engineers were tied into the Ordnance organisation, and the important posts were at provincial and at individual fortress level. The junior permanent ranks were the *ingénieurs-ordinaires*. For most of his active life Vauban pleaded for the creation of a really permanent engineer establishment with army ranks, but his requests got nowhere. Even in France, the home of modern military engineering, those who did the work often went unrecognised.

Other European nations were organised on broadly similar lines, with their engineers as part of the general Ordnance authority and often subservient to the artillery in the field.

ENGINEERING DUTIES

Apart from fortification which will be considered later, engineers in the field were responsible for a number of specialist tasks similar to those they perform today. The most important of these was bridge building, a vital activity for armies that operated in the low-lying Flanders plain with its numerous canals and rivers.

For dealing with streams and areas of marshy ground, temporary expedients could be resorted to. Fascines (bundles of branches) would be placed in the water and covered with a plank roadway. Five such causeways were built under fire over the Nebel stream which divided the two armies at Blenheim.

Larger streams needed more elaborate solutions and every army of the period was accom-

Fig. 65. Pioneers building up a pontoon bridge. The method of construction can be plainly seen from this contemporary engraving.

panied by complete bridging equipment as part of the train. Marlborough had forty pontoons for the 1710 campaign.[6] These were flat bottomed boats some 18 feet long and 5 feet wide, carried upside down on flat four-wheeled carts. Various materials were seemingly used, the basic one being wood, although there is a reference to 'leather' pontoons[7] and other sources mention copper boats and 'tinboat' men. The latter probably refers to the practice of sheathing wooden hulls with copper or zinc.

The pontoon company often had the place of honour on the march, for the obvious reason that they had to be sent off ahead of the troops to prepare a suitable crossing place. The forced march from Lessines to Oudenarde on 11 July 1708 was headed by Cadogan and the pontoon train – without their efforts the Battle of Oudenarde would not have taken place.

The method of constructing such a bridge was fairly simple and is still basically the same today. Once the site had been selected, one man had to swim or wade over with a light line. Once

on the other side he could use this to pull over a heavy cable which he anchored firmly to form the basis of the bridge. The pontoons were then launched one by one, pulled along the cable and anchored fore and aft in a line. In a swift current this was not an easy job.

Once in position, diagonal ropes lashed the pontoons together to form the base for baulks of heavy timber on which was laid a plank roadway. Such a bridge had to be capable of withstanding an enormous weight and great care had to be taken to see that the approaches were passable. The entire Allied army, horses, baggage and artillery, was passed over the Rhine at Coblence in 1704 on their way to the Danube. Such works did, however, collapse on occasions. After the defeat at the Schellenberg in July 1704 the garrison of Donauworth attempted to flee across the Danube on a pontoon bridge, but it gave way and large numbers of men were drowned. A bridge in the right place could mean success for a whole campaign.

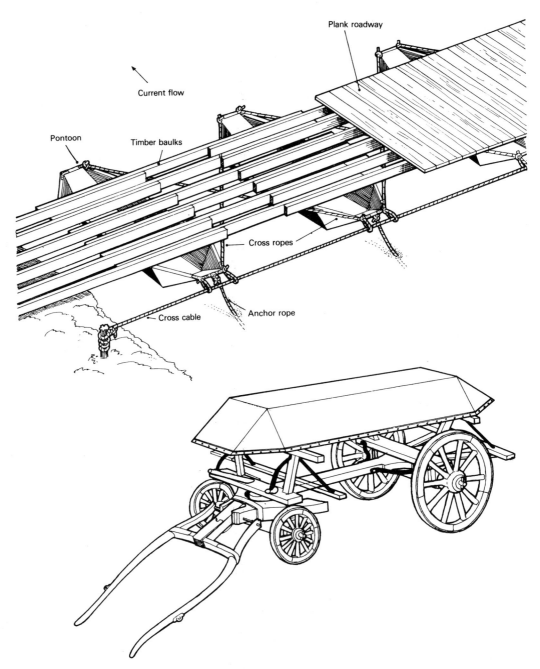

Current flow

Plank roadway

Pontoon

Timber baulks

Cross ropes

Anchor rope

Cross cable

Fig. 66. Bridging equipment. Top, *method of constructing a bridge.* Bottom, *waggon for transporting pontoons (after St Rémy).*

From this it can be seen that the bridging company did not only have to transport the unwieldy pontoons, but also had to carry vast quantities of timber beams and planks, anchors, cordage and tools. Once a bridge was finished with, it had to be dismantled and repacked as quickly as possible, ready for the next river. The loss of such equipment and stores could not easily be made good under the poor supply system of the period.

A typical pontoon company with thirty boats would have some sixty personnel of all ranks under the command of a captain. With one boat per six horse waggon this would entail 180 horses, and if we assume an equal number of waggons for stores, this total doubles to 360 together with their attendant civilian drivers. I estimate that such a train marching nose to tail would occupy just over half a mile of road.

Often coupled with the work of the bridge builders were the activities of the pioneer companies, a definition that was beginning to appear in European armies at the time. A train would have a company of some sixty men whose tasks were plain labouring. St Rémy advocated them for road improvement works in advance of the train on the march. Accompanied by a waggon load of tools they were to fill in pot-holes. They would also have been useful in preparing foundations for the approaches to a bridge site and for digging field fortifications. Naturally, their status in the army as a whole was the lowest of the low!

In peacetime, military engineers often found themselves employed on public or royal works. General Wade, for example, built the network roads in the Highlands of Scotland that are still in use today, and Vauban was largely responsible for the Canal du Midi in the South of France.

FORTIFICATION

Simply defined, fortification is the science of creating an obstacle between oneself and an enemy, and is thus one of the oldest arts known to man. Basically there are two types – field and permanent. The former is concerned with works thrown up in the face of an immediate threat, while the latter comprises works carried out in peacetime to counter a potential threat. Both types were very much a feature of warfare during the early eighteenth century.

FIELD FORTIFICATIONS

It is an old adage in warfare that one man behind a parapet is worth three in the open field, and an outnumbered army is always tempted to dig in to try to redress the negative balance of forces. The classic form of field fortification is the prepared battlefield whereby an army chooses to give battle on a site of its own choosing and which it has improved with pick and shovel.

Such a site could be improved by creating obstacles such as felling trees and interlacing the branches (*abattis*), digging ditches and using the spoil to form breastworks, and making *chevaux des frises*. The latter consisted of a tree stem into which pointed stakes were inserted. A more sophisticated form of field fortification was to build chains of small redoubts (miniature forts). The French resorted to this at Malplaquet where they defended the centre of their line in the open between two woods with a number of such works. For storming such defences, grenadiers were often employed.

Soldiers at the time were notoriously unwilling to wield spades, but large quantities of tools were carried in the trains and issued as required. Mattocks, axes, picks, spades, shovels and billhooks were all available.

On a more grandiose scale were the linear defences which were popular with some armies, notably the French and German. As his style of command was notably aggressive, Marlborough scorned such works and repeatedly proved that they could be penetrated. The basic idea was to link up various permanent fortresses with lines of ditch and rampart running cross country and making use where possible of natural obstacles such as rivers and marshes.

The French constructed these lines to protect their territory from sudden attack before their armies were mobilised, but linear defences suffer from one major flaw. The attacker has the advantage in that he can choose the time and place of his attack and thus can concentrate his forces at the decisive point. The defender, on the other hand, is forced to spread his troops

Fig. 67. Field fortifications. Small redoubts such as these were built by troops in the field for a variety of purposes. Engraving from L'école de Mars, de Guignard, 1725.

thinly along the whole of the line. Unless he can quickly reinforce the threatened sector when the enemy intentions become apparent, his defences are bound to be overwhelmed.

Some of these systems were very extensive. The Lines of Brabant, maintained from 1702 to 1705, covered the 60-odd miles between Namur and Antwerp; the *Ne Plus Ultra* lines built by Marshal Villars in 1710–11, had to defend 90 miles. Shorter, but effective for a number of years, were the Lines of Stollhofen, built by the Imperialists to close the gap between the Rhine and the Black Forest.

Another type of field fortification was the defended camp, built by an army whenever it intended to stay more than a few days in a certain place. They were a direct descendant of marching camps built by the Roman legions when in hostile territory. The engineers were responsible for staking out the perimeter and

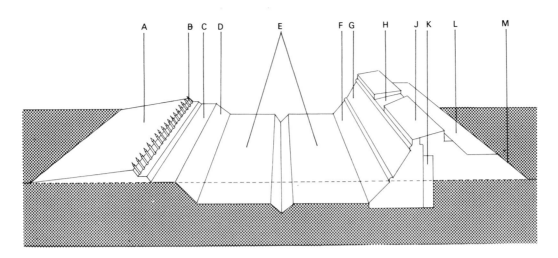

Fig. 68. Profile of a fortification. (A) glacis, (B) palisade, (C) covered way, (D) counterscarp, (E) ditch, (F) escarp, (G) rampart, (H) embrasure, (J) parapet, (K) counterfort, (L) terreplein, (M) talus.

designing the actual defences to be built, which normally consisted of ditch and rampart, perhaps topped with a wooden palisade, and one or more strong gateways.

Such entrenched camps could serve an immediate tactical purpose in that the army was protected from a surprise attack or raid, or a wider strategic purpose. In the latter sense, the mere presence of an army in a particular area, well protected inside a large camp, could influence the operations of the opposition to a considerable degree.

PERMANENT FORTIFICATIONS

Around 1500, when heavy and reasonably mobile artillery had appeared in Europe, the art of fortification underwent a profound change. The high walls and tower-studded ramparts of town defences were gradually replaced by completely new systems of works with a much lower profile. The key element in the design of fortification between 1500 and 1800 was the angle bastion, a projecting artillery platform consisting of two flanks and two faces which

jutted out from a length of curtain wall to provide flanking fire along it. This type of defence, with certain regional variations and 'schools of thought', grew in a rather haphazard way until it began to be rationalised in the middle of the seventeenth century.

The basic idea was to evolve a polygon consisting of a number of angle bastions alternating with lengths of curtain wall, around the object to be protected – in most cases an already existing town – which, when so defended, became a fortress.

Its purpose was to protect the property of those within the defences as an immediate aim, but in time the presence of a fortress took on a strategic significance. No army of the period, with its cumbersome lines of communication, could afford to leave an unreduced fortress in its rear. This in turn led to the large number of sieges that had to be undertaken before an advance could be made. It was therefore in a country's interest to build as many fortresses as possible on its frontiers in order to occupy an invader until a field army could be mobilised.

Obviously, the easier the terrain for the operation of armies, the more fortresses were required. Hence the large number in the vast flat

105

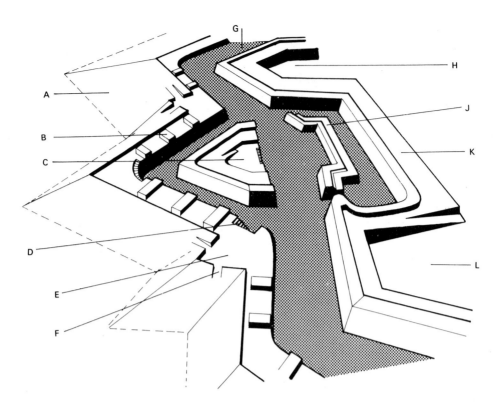

Fig. 69. Vauban's first system. (A) Traverses, (B) Place d'Armes, (C) Exits for sorties, (D) Covered way, (E) Ditch, (F) Demi-Lune, (G) Stairs, (H) Straight-sided bastion, (J) Curtain, (K) Tenaille, (L) Bastion à Orillons.

plain of Flanders, built and garrisoned by the French, the Austrians and the Dutch.

As the power of artillery increased, it became necessary to keep the guns of a besieger further and further away from the main defences. Thus the original simple polygon had to be extended outwards by more and more complicated systems of outworks and ditches, until the plan of the fortress began to resemble some vast geometrical puzzle.

Fortification is a very complicated subject with a jargon all of its own, and there is only space here to sketch in the main points of attack and defence. Once it was decided to build such a work, the engineers arrived and drew up plans, taking into account the natural configuration of the site. A low-lying position could be improved with water defences, and a town perched on a

spur of rock had no great need of extensive outworks.

Let us assume, however, for the purpose of simplification that we have a flat piece of land to be defended without any specific topographical features. Once the plan had been approved, the engineers would stake out the design on the ground with tape, measuring the angles with primitive surveying instruments. After this, the workmen started to excavate the ditches, piling the spoil to form earth ramparts. The area outside the ditch was scarped into a gentle slope running downwards towards the open country (the *glacis*) which was kept deliberately free of any form of cover. The inside walls of the ditch were then faced in masonry or brick and the top of the rampart was formed into a parapet behind which the defenders and their artillery

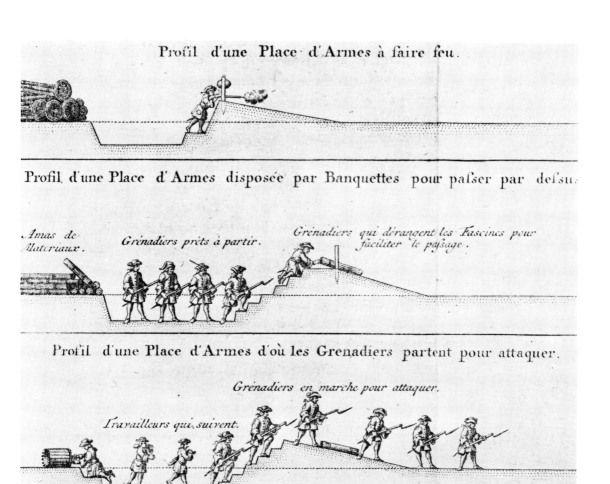

Profil d'une Place d'Armes à faire feu.

Profil d'une Place d'Armes disposée par Banquettes pour passer par dessu.

Amas de Matériaux. Grénadiers prèts à partir. Grénadiers qui dérangent les Fascines pour faciliter le passage.

Profil d'une Place d'Armes d'où les Grenadiers partent pour attaquer.

Grénadiers en marche pour attaquer.

Travailleurs qui suivent.

Fig. 70. Detail from Vauban. Top, profile of a place of arms. Centre, grenadiers assembling for a sortie. Bottom, grenadiers, followed by workmen, sally out to attack the enemy siege works.

could take cover. An outer line of infantry defence was provided for with a breastwork (the covered way) at the top of the glacis, which was usually fronted by a palisade of wooden stakes.

The theoretical basis of this type of fortification was to cover every possible line of approach with flanking fire from artillery and muskets, and to eliminate the slightest area of dead ground where enemy troops could shelter.

No such fortress was impregnable as all could be attacked in some way, and if all else failed and the enemy was prepared to wait, there was the ultimate weapon of starvation. Their real purpose was to gain time and to force the enemy to dissipate his resources on costly siege operations.

SIEGE WARFARE

THE DEFENCE

Once the governor of a fortress realised that he was likely to be besieged, he had to take a number of necessary precautions in order to be able to make an adequate defence. When the attack commenced he would be cut off and would thus lose the initiative. His first duty was to ensure an adequate stock of provisions both for his garrison and the civilian population and to see to the water supply. Civilians could pose a grave problem, especially in territories where loyalties were divided and could frequently exist as a potential fifth column. Ideally, disaffected civilians should have been expelled.

Fig. 71. Officers at a siege. Tapestry by J. de Vos after L. de Hondt.

The governor's next task was to send out parties to gather in any provisions and cut fodder in the surrounding country in order to deny them to the enemy. What could not be collected had to be destroyed, usually resulting in starvation for the peasantry during the following winter.

In addition to the above, the defences had to be repaired where necessary and vast stocks of ammunition and spare parts for the weapons of the garrison had to be laid in. Quantities of tools were required and, most vital of all, there had to be huge stocks of timber for shoring up damaged sections and constructing temporary breastworks.

The quality of the defence depended very much upon the calibre of the governor and the morale of his forces. He could conduct a passive defence, making a token resistance and waiting for the inevitable fall of the place, when he could capitulate with honour in order to save the inhabitants from a sack. This was in accordance with the customs of Baroque warfare when a siege was often just part of an elaborate game played to a well-recognised set of rules.

Alternatively, the governor could conduct an active defence, trying to inflict as much damage as possible on the besiegers and to hinder the progress of their works. He could organise offensive sallies by the garrison, for example, to dismantle trenches and to spike the guns in the opposing batteries. Active mine warfare was another way of upsetting the besiegers. However, if the defence was pushed to the limit and the attackers were forced to storm the place, they were fully entitled by the usages of war to sack the fortress in an orgy of rape and plunder. This ultimate horror was seldom indulged in as it was totally out of character with the warfare of the period. No commander in any army wanted to lose his troops in a town, as it was difficult to get them under control again. Therefore the opposing officers would meet when certain progress had been made with the attack, to agree terms for honourable surrender. They would exchange flowery compliments, nod their wigs together, and the garrison would normally be granted the honours of war. They could march out with flags flying, drums beating, bayonets fixed and matches lit – to signify that they had not been defeated and were still capable of resisting.

THE ATTACK ON A FORTRESS

Once the decision had been made to undertake the siege of a fortress, a vast amount of preliminary work was necessary if the enterprise was to have any chance of success. To besiege a major European fortress during the eighteenth century, a full field army was required – as an average, 60,000 men. The latter had to be fed, and in a static warfare situation lasting anything up to three months and with the surround-

ing countryside soon stripped bare, this meant that all supplies had to be delivered – even including forage for the horses. Vast magazines had to be laid down at a convenient distance and supply convoys organised, which was where Marlborough's civilian contractors came into their own.

St Rémy gives some extremely interesting statistics of supplies and material required for a theoretical army of 60,000 men for an assumed 40-day period.[8] Such a force and its attendant labour squads would need 3,300,000 ration issues! If we assume that a basic ration was 2 lbs of bread and 1 lb of meat plus 2 pints of beer per man per day, a vastly complicated transport scheme would have been required. However, there were also the stores to be taken into consideration. St Rémy lists 550,000 cubic feet of timber for constructing gun platforms, revetting trenches, etc., 18,000 hand tools, 4,000 baskets (*gabions*) and enormous quantities of rope, nails, sandbags, etc.

The real requirement, however, was for sufficient heavy guns to batter a breach in the defences and for enough ammunition to keep them firing for a long period. As we have seen, the siege train did not march with the army, but was held in reserve at a suitable location to be able to move up when required. Such a train was extremely cumbersome and, where possible, water transport was used. Large fleets of flat-bottomed barges were used in Flanders for transporting the guns and their equipment from siege to siege, but at times abysmal roads had to be used.

The 'Great Convoy' that travelled from Brussels to Lille in July 1708 moved in two sections, covering some 15 miles of roads. The eight siege guns (mostly 24-pounders) needed twenty horses each to pull them, and the twenty mortars each required sixteen horses, plus some 3,000 four horse waggons full of stores and ammunition. The duties of a siege train were defined as follows:

'The demi-cannon [24-pounders] are the most generally useful pieces in the attack on a fortress:

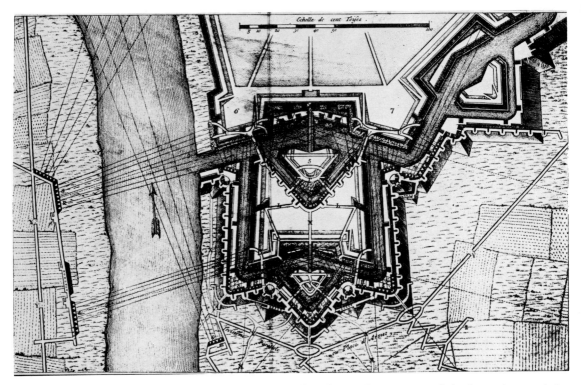

Fig. 72. Example of siege works, from Vauban. This shows the position of the batteries, and the third parallel has been placed in front of a hornwork.

they breach and shatter the walls, and the fragments are then broken up by the quarter-cannon [16- and 12-pounders]. The falconets and regimental pieces strike at the embrasures. . . . They are also the most suitable pieces for shooting red-hot shot.'[9]

For his 40-day siege, St Rémy calculated 40,000 rounds of 24-pounder shot, 16,000 for the smaller guns and 9,000 mortar bombs. Nearly a million pounds of powder was required to maintain such a fire programme.

Once it became clear that sufficient material would be available, the army could begin to advance towards the objective, leaving the siege train to catch up later. For purposes of basic calculation of *matériel*, Vauban reckoned that a full textbook siege (*siège en grande règle*) would last 48 days,[10] and one of his successors, the French engineer Cormontaigne, went even further, calculating the length of resistance that could be put up by each type of fortress.

There were, however, methods which could

be employed short of a formal siege. If a fortress was unprepared or not expecting to be attacked, there was always the chance that a party of raiders could get possession of one of the gates. In 1702, the Elector of Bavaria wanted to reduce the Imperial fortress of Ulm, but

'to lay siege to a fortified town of this description was a doubtful business. The best means, therefore, to attain our end was to surprise it by some stratagem, for though the Elector's army was strong, it was not strong enough to invest the town and at the same time provide against the relieving force that the Empire would surely send.'[11]

A group of raiders was first sent into the town disguised as traders, while three regiments of dragoons were hidden in the vicinity. At the given time, the 'civilians' overpowered the guards and admitted their comrades who secured the town.

Another method was for a small group to

Fig. 73. Fascinade. *Cavalry engaged in collecting branches to make fascines, while in the distance a siege is in progress. Engraving after Guerard.*

enter the town by escalade (the use of scaling ladders), and if all else failed indiscriminate bombardment could be resorted to. By destroying their houses, it was hoped that the civilian morale would crack and thus force the governor to capitulate. An easy victory represented enormous savings in time and materials.

However, once a siege had to be undertaken, it progressed along well laid-down lines which had developed as a result of practical experience. By the latter part of the seventeenth century, the earlier haphazard methods had been formalised to such an extent by Vauban that there was little scope for innovation or private initiative.

The besiegers' first task was to cut off the fortress from contact with the outside world, to prevent it being reinforced. As the army approached, advance cavalry patrols would be posted on all roads leading into the place, and then the troops would gradually surround it. Once in position they dug a line of entrenchments all the way around to guard against sallies by the garrison (lines of contravallation). If there was any danger of an enemy relief force

appearing on the scene, they would excavate another line (circumvallation) facing outwards. In between the two the besiegers' camp would be established, with horse lines, storage depots, artillery parks, magazines and tented camps. In the event of a relief attempt, the attackers might find themselves in turn besieged in their own camp – caught between the fortress garrison and the relieving army.

It was then up to the army commander and his senior engineers to examine the position and to choose the point or points of attack which was usually directed towards the salient of a bastion – in the case of a more complicated fortress, at the ravelin between two bastions. The issue was further complicated if the fortress, as well as protecting the town, had a separate citadel. The normal method in such cases was to first reduce the actual town defences and then proceed to the citadel.

During this reconnaissance stage, the siege park would be a hive of activity as the necessary stores were made ready and the working parties were divided up into shifts. The fireworkers had to fill the bombs and prepare the

111

fuzes, usually protected by 'laboratories' covered by plank and turf roofs. Ideally, the park was situated out of range of the guns of the fortress at a distance of some 2,000 yards from the main defences.

The troops not employed at the time on manning the defences of the camp were also kept busy. Samuel Noyes wrote that 'orders were given . . . for a detachment of every Battalion to go this morning into the woods in the rear and make some 500 fascines 6 feet long and bring them to their own front whence the Horse were to carry them to the siege.'[12] (Fascines were long bundles of branches that were used for filling ditches and stiffening earth parapets.) Another item required in large numbers was the gabion. This was a woven basket about 2 feet in diameter and 3 feet high, which when filled with earth provided excellent frontal protection for batteries. They were made by the troops, who were usually paid extra on a piecework basis.

At this stage, actual operations could begin. In overall charge of operations was the Director of the Trenches (in France, the *tranchée major*), responsible for each shift for round-the-clock working, while the 'major-general of the day' commanded the actual troops engaged in doing the spade work. The reason for the trenches being necessary was that troops could not advance in open order up the bare glacis under fire from the fortress, which would only have resulted in mass slaughter – those that got to the top would have tumbled into the ditch. Therefore they had to dig their way up to the rim of the ditch, descend into it and cross it before tackling the main rampart.

The start of operations was known as the 'opening of the trenches'. During the chosen night large numbers of men would march out from the camp armed with spades, and dig a trench parallel and in an arc to the sector to be attacked. This then formed the basis for a garrison to protect further work and as a storage space for stores. From this, a number of saps or zig-zag approach trenches would be dug in order to gain ground up the glacis.

Service in the trenches was a hazardous occupation and casualties among the supervising engineers could be heavy. In self-protection, they tended to wear somewhat cumbersome body armour that would not have improved their mobility. Heads were protected by a *tranchée helm* which was an extremely heavy pot helmet with metal face protection bars. Some engineers wore a normal cuirass, but special trench armour was available consisting of both back and breast plates to which heavy steel skirt pieces were attached. Besides the obvious dangers from gunfire, the trenches were unhealthy places, damp and cold. To keep the workers going, frequent issues of free spirits had to be made. If you had to wield a spade, it was better to do so when half drunk.

The first batteries were established just in front of the first parallel, both for mortars and guns. The former aimed their bombs at the interior, while the latter did their best to dismantle the fortress guns on the ramparts. The usual number of guns in a battery was six, emplaced behind a solid earth parapet stiffened with gabions, in which embrasures had been cut. The actual guns were positioned on solid wooden platforms to stop them from sinking into the mire, and their powder supply was stored to the rear in earth covered expense magazines.

A sap was started by one man advancing from the parallel, pushing a mantlet or shield on wheel in front of him. A variant of this was the sap roller or *gabion farci* which was a gabion that could rotate on an axle and was pushed ahead by a handle. He dug a shallow trench and placed the spoil in a gabion which he positioned beside him in the direction of the fortress. Three more men came behind him, deepening the sap and crowning the row of gabions with fascines and piled earth. Vauban reckoned that such a sap could progress 160 yards in 24 hours, which was an astonishing speed when one considers that the men were working under fire.

The second parallel was dug some 300 yards from the top of the glacis, and guns were man-

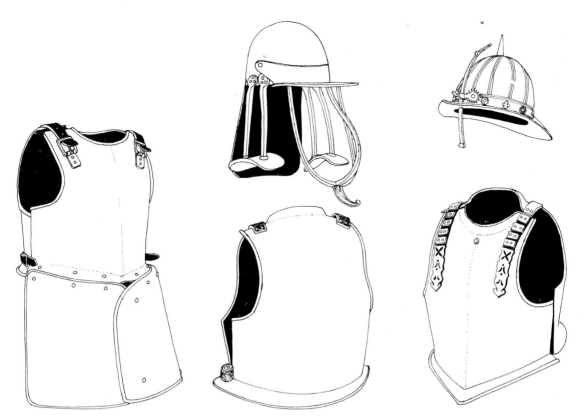

Fig. 74. Left, *English engineer's armour, circa 1680.* Centre top, *helmet for same.* Centre *and* left bottom, *carbine proof armour as supplied to siege train, circa 1700.* Top right, *Vauban's siege helmet.*

handled forward to form new batteries. It was at this stage that the defenders might be tempted to make a sortie, dashing out at night to interrupt the working parties and spike the guns. This common expression meant just what it said. The easiest way to disable a gun was to hammer a metal spike down the touch-hole and then to use the ramrod to bend over the end that stuck down into the bore. When one had more time, a shot well wrapped in cloth could be rammed right down the bore into the chamber. A permanent job could be achieved by loading in as much powder as possible and then selecting a shot with a good tight fit. When this had been hammered in and the gun touched off, the resulting burst must have been most gratifying to the perpetrators.

However, not all activity was necessarily on the surface. Mining was frequently resorted to by an attacker, and countermining by the de-

fender. A well-planned fortress would have a network of countermine tunnels dug under the glacis, the ends of which could be charged with barrels of powder and exploded under the besiegers' works. The only remedy was for the attackers themselves to dig down and try to reach the countermines with a blast of their own. This was a terrible form of warfare, as the two sides would sometimes meet underground and do battle with pick handles and shovels. It was also extremely dangerous, as tunnels could cave in without warning or be destroyed by a well-placed counter charge (*camouflet*). The miners were often issued with helmets made of toughened leather to give them some protection from roof falls.

Deep mining called for skilled men, and the mining companies were usually recruited from men used to working in the coal fields. The aim was to sink a shaft from the glacis and then to

113

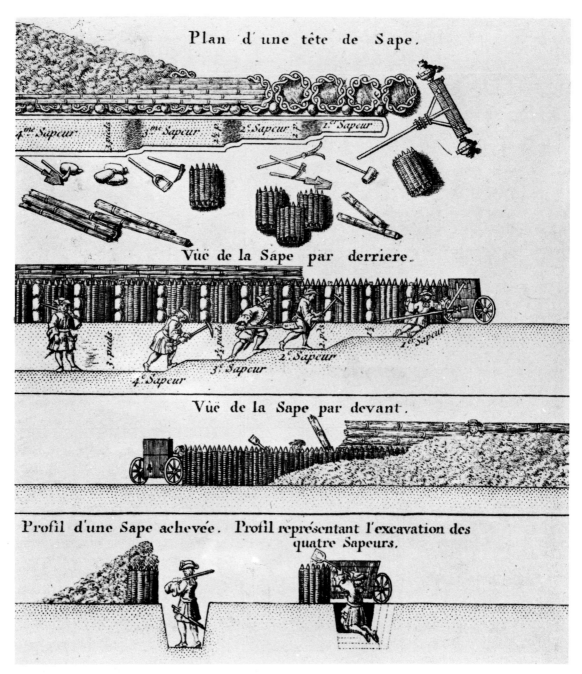

Fig. 75. Sapping techniques, after Vauban. Note the tools used and the method of forming parapets with gabions and fascines.

tunnel under the ditch to a position below the rampart where the charge would be placed in a hollowed out chamber. Vast amounts of timber were required for revetting the tunnel, and a grave problem was the disposal of the spoil.

Secrecy was essential if the operation was to have any chance of success.

The men usually worked in teams of miners and carpenters, and given good ground could advance some 15 feet per day. This was

114

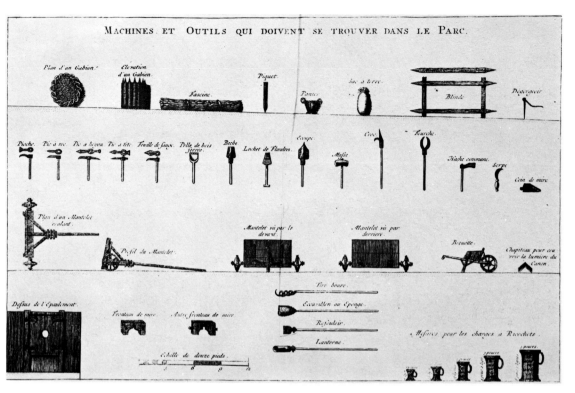

Fig. 76. Engineering tools, after Vauban. This shows various types of pick and shovel, as well as artillery items and a mantlet to be pushed out in front to protect the sappers.

much slower than comparable surface work, and was only resorted to when the men on top were unable to progress easily. Assuming then that the tunnel managed to proceed under the ditch to the right spot, the chamber was crammed with powder packed in barrels or sacks. It was not until somewhat later that scientific calculations were made concerning the amount of powder and the methods of packing that were needed to create a specific effect.

Once in place, the mine was tamped back down the tunnel by being back-filled with earth in order to force the weight of the explosion upwards. As fuze, a long thin canvas hose called a *saucisson* filled with powder was led back to the mouth of the shaft where it could be touched off when required.

In an assault on a position during a siege where there was a suspicion that the garrison might have countermines, the capture of any shafts and the means of ignition were of prime importance. At Charleroi in 1693, Colonie commanded such a storming party of grenadiers which was visited by Vauban just before they attacked.

'M. de Vauban passed about this time, and assured us with a confident air that we should make short work of the half-moon battery, that it was defended only by a rabble, and that he was not at all sure that it was mined, and that even if it were so we should so surprise the enemy that they would never have time to put fire to the trains. He cautioned us, however, to make a rapid inspection of the work on entering to prove this point, and told us that M. de Luxembourg [the French commander] had promised a reward to anyone bringing him a port-fire or quick match . . .'.[13]

In the meanwhile, on the surface, the saps had reached to within some 70 yards of the crest of the glacis or covered way. At this distance the third parallel was established, around which would be sited the close-range batteries for making the vital breach in the rampart. The

115

Fig. 77. Musketeer (Dutch) firing from behind a screen padded with a woolsack. After an engraving by F. H. W. Kuypers.

next stage was to 'crown' or capture the covered way by effecting a 'lodgement'. First, however, the defenders had to be expelled and this was often the bloodiest part of any siege. The grenadiers would be formed up in the parallel and in the advance saps, while the mortars would fire a hail of stones and bombs to decimate the opposition. Not all would be killed and desperate hand-to-hand fighting with grenade and bayonet could well ensue. The remaining defenders with the ditch behind them had little chance of regaining safety.

Once on the covered way, the result of the siege was more or less a foregone conclusion. The 24-pounders would be emplaced along the top of the glacis and begin to pound a breach in the retaining masonry of the rampart, the falling debris helping to fill the ditch. A 'practicable' breach was usually defined as being wide enough for four horsemen to ride abreast, or alternatively, with a gentle enough slope for men to march up without having to use their hands to support themselves.

It was at this stage in the proceedings that the governor could best beat the *chamade*, the signal for a parley, or the besiegers' commander could 'send a trumpet' to request negotiations or 'summon the place'. Sending a trumpet was another of those mediaeval throw-backs recalling the days of heralds. If the governor agreed that the breach was 'practicable' then he would

accept terms and withdraw with honour, which was the sensible thing to do in that rational age.

However, if he refused, the next obstacle for the attackers was to bring down the rampart even more and cross the ditch. If the breaching batteries were not having much effect, and the ditch was a dry one, another form of mining could be resorted to. This was known as 'attaching the miner', and two or three intrepid men would scamper across the floor of the ditch and hack a few bricks or stones out of the revetment of the escarp. Then, working in relays and hoping to remain unobserved, they would tunnel their way into the earth core of the rampart and place a number of mines. If the garrison managed to discover what was going on they would countermine from the interior or try to block the shaft by dropping stones or soil.

Dry and wet ditches each had advantages and disadvantages. A dry ditch was fairly easy to cross and could easily be filled with rubble brought down from the rampart. A wet ditch, where the terrain permitted the use of water, was difficult for an enemy to cross, but it could freeze over in winter. If the water in it was static, it was a breeding ground for disease in those days of primitive sanitation. Ideally, where a fortress was situated on a river, sluices could be built to permit the stream to be diverted into the ditch only when required, and this had the additional advantage that the current would scour the refuse from the ditch – making enemy bridging attempts difficult.

The 'descent of the ditch' having been decided upon, a number of ramps were cut down from the covered way to the floor of the ditch if dry, and if wet, to water level. The 'passage' of a dry bed was made by means of the usual sapping technique until the spoil from the dismantled rampart was reached, during which time the mortars would be busy trying to discourage any of the fortress guns that were still firing from the flanking bastions. In the case of a wet ditch, a causeway had to be built across it, which was a lengthy process. Materials such as baskets of stones and fascines had to be brought up through the siege works and passed down the ramps via a human chain. If the water was very deep, the only solution was to build a bridge, which again had to be assembled in sections from materials brought laboriously to the spot.

Once the ditch was ready to be crossed, all was ready for the storm. The grenadiers would be positioned, armed to the teeth for the dash across the ditch and up the breach – behind which the defenders would be waiting, covered by hastily constructed earth and wooden retrenchments. The mortars would bring down a hail of bombs to keep the garrison occupied while the grenadiers got to grips. If a siege was taken to this ultimate stage, tempers would be up and no mercy would be shown. Officers too would be up in the forward line eager for glory and recognition. It was the dream of any young ensign to plant his regimental colours on the ruins of a stormed breach.

Far back in 1672, a young captain then named simply John Churchill had distinguished himself at the siege of Maastricht when serving in the French army under the Duke of Monmouth. He took part in a storm and in repelling a sortie by the garrison, and his courage was brought to the notice of his later foe, Louis XIV.[14]

However, the final words can be left to Captain Parker who has given us an account of the storming of Fort St Michael at Venlo in 1702. What follows is a classic example of a fleeting opportunity being seized and exploited by a hardy group of men.

'About four in the afternoon the signal was given, and according to our orders we rushed up to the covert-way [sic]; the enemy gave us scattering fire only, and away they ran. We jumped into the covert-way, and ran after them. They made to a ravelin, which covered the curtain of the fort in which were a Captain and 60 men. We seeing them get into the ravelin, pursued them, got in with them, and soon put most of them to the sword. They that escaped us fled over a small wooden bridge, that led over the moat to the fort; and here like madmen without fear or wit, we pursued them over that tottering bridge, exposed to the fire of the great and small shot of the body of the fort. However, we got over the faussebraye [a defended ledge at the base of a rampart], where we had nothing for it but to take the fort or die. They that fled before us climbed up by the long grass, that grew out of the fort [a good

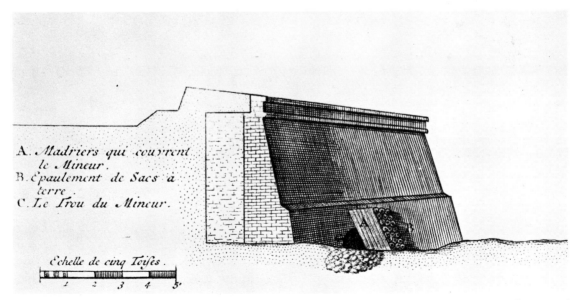

A. *Madriers qui couvrent le Mineur.*
B. *Épaulement de Sacs à terre.*
C. *Le Trou du Mineur.*

Échelle de cinq Toises.

Fig. 78. *Attaching the miner, after Vauban. The miners have crossed the ditch and have burrowed into the escarp of a fortification.*

117

governor would have had this cut!], so we climbed after them. Here we were hardput to it to pull out the palisades, which pointed down upon us from the parapet; and was it not for the great surprise and consternation of those within, we could never have surmounted this very point. But as soon as they saw us at this work, they quitted the rampart, and retired down to the parade . . . where they laid down their arms and cried for quarter, which was readily granted them'.[15]

This brief chapter on military engineering has been but a sketch of what is a highly complex and technical subject which became almost a way of life for those engaged in it. Its ritual aspects and jargon were so beautifully satirised by Laurence Sterne in *Tristram Shandy*, whose father in speaking to his brother said:

'. . . But I wish the whole science of fortification, with all its inventors, at the devil; – it has been the death of thousands – and it will be mine in the end, – I would not . . . have my brains so full of saps, mines, blinds, gabions, palisadoes, ravelins, half-moons, and such trumpery, to be proprietor of Namur, and of all the towns in Flanders with it.'[16]

NOTES

1 For an excellent examination of this whole subject, see Duffy, *Fire and Stone*.
2 Howard. 72.
3 Scouller. 186.
4 Colonie. 102–3.
5 Quoted by Scouller. 185.
6 Chandler. *Art of War*. 229.
7 Noyes. Letter X. *JSAHR*. 1959.
8 St Rémy. Vol. II. Chapter V.
9 Miethen, M. *Artilleriae Recentior Praxis*. Frankfurt. 1683.
10 Vauban. 51–4.
11 Colonie. 96–102.
12 Noyes. Op. cit.
13 Colonie. 33.
14 Churchill. Vol. I. 89–91.
15 Parker. 22–3.
16 *Tristram Shandy*. Book II. Chapter 12.

Fig. 79. La marche. *J de Vos after L. de Hondt. This tapestry shows an army on the march. Note the sutler in the foreground offering her wares, and various women and children.*

ON THE MARCH

TRANSPORT

The speed and range of any eighteenth-century army were determined by the ability of its baggage and artillery to keep pace with it. A further limitation was the dreadful state of the roads and the vast numbers of horses and waggons required. Highly competent staff work was required if an army was not to become immobilised and thus lose the initiative. Even leaving aside the transport of the guns and the stores belonging to the Train, the rest of the army still required an enormous amount of miscellaneous transport.

In the period under discussion, and indeed until the beginning of the nineteenth century, the English army had no central transport authority or organisation. The body responsible was the inevitable Board or Ordnance, staffed by civilians and only indirectly answerable to commanders in the field. The Lieutenant-General of the Ordance was actually responsible for the movement of the various Trains, delegating this duty to the Waggon-Master-General who was a member of the Commander-in-Chief's staff in the field. For other forms of transport, however, the commander on the spot was responsible for finding it. Expeditionary forces going abroad were not supplied with carts – they had to obtain them at their destination. In fairness, however, one must recognise that the shipping industry at the time was not extensive enough to cope, and carrying the troops themselves was enough of a headache.

A commander had to have vehicles to move such items as baggage, stores, bread, other foodstuffs, the sick and wounded, and all the other items required by his troops. In addition, he still had to oversee the requirements of his Train. Thus the only answer was to hire or impress civilian drivers or boys, with their animals and carts. Such people had no interest in the cause for which the army was fighting, and were thus regarded as being potentially unreliable. Large numbers of troops had to be detached to guard them not only from the enemy, but also to stop them from running away. This is delightfully illustrated in the Wynendaele Tapestry at Blenheim Palace, where in the foreground, a sergeant of the Royal Scots can be seen threatening a driver with his halberd.

Part of the Allied transport requirement was provided by the main bread contractors on a long term basis, while the rest had to be obtained locally. Often such levies could only be hired for the distance of a three-day march from their homes, which must have entailed frequent trans-shipment of loads. If drivers and vehicles were not obtainable on a voluntary basis, impressment would be resorted to. On the whole, the troops directly under the command of Marlborough fared pretty well for transport as he had a well-stocked treasury and could pay cash. Other armies, especially the French who paid in tallies or promissory notes to be redeemed at some future date, were not viewed with so much favour by the peasantry. The

Fig. 80. Four-wheeled carts after St Rémy. Types of chariot *and* charette *used by the French artillery trains at the end of the seventeenth century.*

situation of the English in the Peninsula side-show was catastrophic.

Extensive use was made of mules and pack-horses, which had less difficulty in negotiating the pot-holed roads but were limited in the loads that they could carry. Officers, for example, were entitled to a 'bat horse' (from the French *cheval de bât*), from which the modern term batman originates, as an officer's servant was responsible for leading the bat horse.

Wheeled transport broke down into two basic types. Firstly, there was the high two-wheeled tumbril, which was commonly referred to as a 'marlbrouk' on the Continent – as legend has it Marlborough invented these light sprung vehicles. They could be either open with the load covered by a tarpaulin or be fitted with a rounded canvas tilt, and were pulled by two horses in tandem. The Wynendaele Tapestry shows such a cart in some detail. It had large iron-shod wheels with high plank sides, the rear horse being placed between shafts and the lead horse loose coupled by chains running from a decorated collar. The driver sits on the back of the lead horse with his legs dangling over the side, holding the reins in his left hand and brandishing a whip in his right.

The other type of vehicle was a four-wheeled agricultural cart with openwork sides. Paintings show them usually pulled by six horses harnessed in pairs, and their average load capacity was some 1,200 pounds of stores, although they were also used for the wounded.

The basic European road soon became furrowed by wheel ruts anything up to a foot deep. As a result, vehicles in different areas became in course of time and according to local custom standardised to a particular distance between the wheels. Muller, writing on artillery in the 1750s stated that artillery waggons were built to the so-called Flanders width of 4 feet 8 inches – which in turn became the standard European railway gauge.[1]

In the Netherlands and Flanders, water transport was used where possible for the movement of heavy stores such as guns and bulk ammunition. Flat bottomed barges towed by teams of horses made slow but steady progress along the network of navigable rivers and canals. As so many fortresses were built to control river crossings, they had to be cleared one by one so as to free the lines of communication. The French even had a small fleet of armed gunboats on the Scheldt, and in the autumn of 1708 while the siege of Lille was in progress, a mini naval war was fought among the inundations around Ostend. The French used armed rowing galleys to interrupt the English supply convoys which were being ferried from the port across the flooded lowlands until they could be transferred to waggons on high ground.

Although no transport was physically issued to the armies, the English army operated administratively with a system of allowances. These were theoretical amounts and were represented as a sum of money that could be claimed – at a later date. As Captain-General, Marlborough was entitled to twenty-seven waggons, three carts and twenty baggage horses.[2] He also had his magnificent coach in attendance, drawn by six horses, with a coachman on the box and a footman clinging on to the back. For a man of such modest tastes in the field, it is unlikely that he used as much, especially as he was always encouraging his subordinates to cut down on their own baggage. Indeed, he was criticised by some of his contemporaries for his supposed meanness and for the lack of state which he kept, which in the eighteenth century was a crime for a high nobleman. Dukes and Princes were expected to entertain and to spend money lavishly. He did, however, carry a set of valuable plate for unavoidable state occasions, but preferred to dine with a small group.[3]

In Spain, Peterborough is said to have had seventeen waggons, more than fifty mules and several horses, which with the baggage they carried were estimated to be worth £8,000 in the currency of the time.[4]

Most senior officers were hampered by vast amounts of impedimenta. Mérode-Westerloo says that after Blenheim in the retreat through Ulm, he lost 'in addition to my carts, all my field furniture, chairs, tables, beds, utensils, field ovens – the lot.' Note the use of the plural in referring to beds! However, all was not lost, for his 'most vital possessions' were carried by two dozen mules which he managed to save.[5] He stated quite definitely that he had thirteen spare chargers with him at Blenheim, and that between there and Brussels, he lost ninety-seven

Fig. 81. The French leaving Augsburg in 1704. Note the bat-horse in the foreground. Engraving by G. Ph. Rugendas.

horses and their harnesses through battle and sickness. On the night before the battle he had taken up quarters in a farm near the village of Blenheim (Blindheim in correct German), where his 'retinue' had spread carpets on the floor and had set up his curtained bed.

At battalion level, the allowances were not quite so generous. Each unit had its waggon-master, a subaltern or nco, who was responsible for supervision. The heavy battalion baggage moved with the main column, but each colonel was allowed one or two carts to accompany the troops. According to Marlborough, the transport allowance in 1707 was fifty waggons per 10,000 men, while in the summer of 1704 he was trying to provide four waggons per battalion.[6] The main item to be carried at battalion level was bread, as an army was expected to be able to carry a four-day supply before a halt was made for fresh baking. However, there were such bulky items as tents, the headquarters equipment, the surgeon's stores and probably the cooking pots for the men.

Remembering that the ration of bread was 2 lbs per day per per man and a unit numbered on average 800, for four days this meant a weight of 6,400 lbs. At an average loading of 1,200 lbs per waggon, the battalion would have needed for its bread alone on the first day of a four-day march, at least five waggons. Therefore the allowances stipulated above must have been supplemented in some way or the men had to carry rations on their backs.

The numbers of vehicles and horses attached to any army at any one time cannot be accurately calculated, but a few examples of the magnitude of the problem can be cited. Very much depended on the state of the road and the amount of equipment to be carried. The Allied army which marched to the Danube in the summer of 1704 was accompanied by 1,700 waggons drawn by 5,000 horses – for a force of some 40,000 troops.[7] St. Rémy's theoretical train of fifty field guns referred to in the chapter on artillery needed 1,225 horses to draw the actual guns, plus 220 waggons loaded with ammunition and other stores. The Prince of

Hesse-Cassel's 13-pounders needed thirteen horses each and the 3-pounders three or four each. His howitzers were each pulled by eight horses and each gun needed three carts to carry powder and bombs.

Although published somewhat later than the period under consideration (1741), Captain Thomas Binning in his book *A Light to the Art of Gunnery*, wrote that over good going a horse could pull 500 lbs of metal, but on poor roads only 350, while an 'indifferent' man could pull 80. His Train 'in order of march' comprised six demi-culverins with powder and shot in waggons (total 19,200), six demi-cannon (27,000) and two cannon (14,000). This gave a total weight of 60,200, plus transport for tools, matches etc. Divide this sum by 80 and we discover that 752 'indifferent' men would have been required to pull it.

THE ARMY ON THE MARCH

From the above, it can be seen that for every 'tooth', an army of the early eighteenth century had a vast amount of 'tail'. In the various meagre sources concerning the English army at the time, there are no references to livestock 'on the hoof', but such living rations may well have been the responsibility of the sutlers — meat was not provided by the authorities as soldiers were expected to buy it from their subsistence allowance. However, the Rev. Samuel Noyes enjoyed a good 'broth from boiled meat' after the battle of Blenheim — made from captured French bullocks.

The distance that could be travelled in any one day was limited to a large extent by the speed of the baggage and artillery. Referring to the March to the Danube, Parker wrote: 'We frequently marched three, sometimes four days, successively, and halted a day. We generally began our march about three in the morning, proceeded about four leagues, or four and a half each day, and reached our ground about nine.'[8] This rate of 12 to 14 miles a day does not seem much when one considers what modern soldiers carrying roughly the same weight can achieve, but it compares favourably with the performance of Frederick the Great's troops some forty years later. They were capable 'of moving a dozen miles a day for a week or two at a stretch. In normal circumstances half of that distance was a more reasonable average, given the exigencies of supply and the necessity of resting for one day in three or four.'[9]

By shedding baggage, however, Marlborough's infantry could on occasions put up a dazzling performance. When forcing the *Ne Plus Ultra* lines in August 1711, they managed to march 36 miles in 16 hours, more or less non-stop — although considerable numbers dropped from exhaustion on the way.

This idea of rising at the crack of dawn and completing the daily march early, was to make use of the time before the sun got up. Just imagine marching in high summer dressed in a long thick coat and festooned with some 50 lbs of loose equipment. It also left plenty of time during the rest of the day for the normal business of the army, which in many ways was connected with the fight for survival. In the days before pre-packed combat rations, motorised field kitchens and a reliable supply system, most of the troops were engaged in obtaining something to eat for themselves (and their horses) and cooking it.

Marlborough's standing orders laid down that on the day of a march the normal 'Reveille' was not beaten. Instead, the drums beat the 'General', upon which all were to dress and prepare to move off. This was followed by the 'Assembly' which was the signal for striking the tents and packing the baggage, calling in the outpost guards and standing to arms.[10]

In view of the few and poor roads, an army was frequently forced to march in a single column strung out over several miles, and the precautions taken against attack would depend on the nearness of the enemy. Normally, a cavalry screen would be sent out well in advance, and if rivers were to be crossed the pontoons would be well up in the van together with a strong escort. They would be

Fig. 82. Leaving winter quarters (Guerard). A group of soldiers leaving the town where they have spent the winter. Note the man on the cart trying to steal a pigeon.

followed by the bulk of the infantry, the flanks guarded by roving cavalry squadrons, and in some cases by an advance artillery detachment. The artillery and the baggage trains would occupy the rear with the sutlers' waggons relegated to the tail end of the column. A strong rearguard would follow along behind to scoop up any stragglers, and when retreating pursued by the enemy, these troops had the place of honour.

At times, however, an army could separate and move along parallel roads, formed into *ad hoc* divisions. When moving in peaceful country, other solutions were possible. On the way to the Danube in 1704, Marlborough sent the artillery and infantry to make their own way under the command of his brother, General Churchill, while he himself moved ahead with the cavalry. If the artillery was split, a number of guns with enough ammunition in waggons for immediate use could be placed near the head of the column.

The bane of any eighteenth-century army was desertion, and therefore great precautions had to be taken not only to prevent surprise by

the enemy, but to stop the men voting with their feet. Army commanders preferred to march in flat open country and tended to avoid woods, narrow defiles and broken country where possible. Such features allowed men to melt away too easily.

With the advance guard was the Quartermaster-General or his deputy together with a small staff who were responsible for finding the next camp site and marking it out ready for the army to take up their allotted quarters. The army commander and his staff also rode well in front in order to be able to make decisions on the spot and alter the direction of the march if required. If in contact with the enemy and actively seeking a battle, he had to keep his troops closed up, as wheeling from column into line could take several hours, giving the opposition time to slink off.

Winston Churchill called the Allied army on the way to the Danube a 'scarlet caterpillar' which was probably fair, although many of the armies of the period would have presented a pretty ragged appearance. March discipline was of paramount importance because of the

Fig. 83. On the march (Guerard). A realistic view of early eighteenth century soldiers shouldering their belongings and loot.

tendency to straggle and thus disintegrate into a rabble. All the orders of the period concentrate on keeping together as a cohesive force, which applied especially to the artillery, as the guns were useless wihout the right waggons being in the right place at the right time.

Prime disturbers were often the private baggage trains of senior officers. In August 1705, Parker recorded:

'We were now drawing near to the enemy, and His Grace sent orders that the English train of artillery should make all possible haste up to him: but as they were just entering upon a narrow defile, Slangenberg came up to the head of them, and stopped them for some hours, until his baggage had passed on before them, a thing never known before even for the King's baggage. And this delay it was which prevented the Duke from attacking the enemy. . . .'[11]

To bring the artillery forward was a considerable feat. First the message had to be passed back and orders given to the infantry to move themselves and their waggons off the road. Then the Train got under way with the Gentlemen of the Ordnance and the other officers marching alongside. The gunners and their assistants would be urging on the drivers and applying liberal coats of 'train grease' to the creaking axle trees. The accompanying fusiliers would help to heave at the drag ropes if a gun threatened to get stuck and pioneers would be at the ready to fill in the worst of the pot-holes. Company commanders were enjoined to patrol up and down the column and not to permit anybody 'on the guns, nor permit any baggage to be put upon them'.

At battalion level, there were also exact rules and regulations, and it is probable that they were adhered to. A French infantry battalion marched in order of its thirteen companies, the grenadiers leading and the drums divided equally between front and rear. The colour party marched snugly in the centre. Out in front came the officers, spaced at 'spontoon length' and the men marched six abreast with the sergeants on the flanks – to apprehend stragglers and would-be deserters.[12]

The system was more or less the same in the English and German armies. Once the tents had been struck and the baggage loaded, the men stood to arms in companies facing the front. On the order to march being given, the advance guard would set off and the officers and nco's would take post. The men would then turn into column and march off to the beat of the drums. Each battalion was ordered to provide a rearguard of a subaltern and twenty-four men to take up stragglers. Kane made the following comments concerning infantry on the march:

'As soon as the Colonel has sent off his advance-guard he orders the officer of the rear-guard to take care of the baggage or convoy and see that they keep good order in their march and close to the regiment. This officer is also to detach a sergeant and twelve men to keep a proper distance in the rear of him, and both of them to look sharp lest the enemy may lie in ambush by the advance-guard and come out in hopes of surprising us in the rear. . . . Nor is it to be conceived what a panic seizes a body of foot when they are surprised after such a manner. Nothing but confusion attends them on such occasions and they are cut to pieces before they can get into order. Nor on the other hand can it be conceived with what courage and resolution a body of Foot will be animated when they find themselves in good order and posture of defence.'[13]

It could sound all very romantic when one visualises the scarlet clad troops marching to the beat of the drums in the early morning sunlight, but there was another, darker side to the story — bad weather, as the following extracts from Blackader show:

'We marched all yesterday, all night and all this day. There was a constant heavy rain most of the time, which made the roads very bad. We were sometimes four hours marching half a mile. I was thirty hours on horseback . . .!

'We left camp at three o'clock in the afternoon, and marched all night, a tedious and fatiguing march. We continued on our journey 'till three in the afternoon the next day. . . . It poured down a heavy rain, and the cavalry had so broken the ways, that the men marched in clay and dirt to the knees almost the whole day, for four leagues. There was hardly a hundred men of a regiment with the colours that night.'[14]

Little is known about the women who accom-panied the armies of the period, but each battalion would have had a number of them as well as a few children. They did the washing and probably helped with the cooking. Orders were issued in the English army prohibiting them from riding on the baggage waggons, but it is possible that exceptions were made, knowing the soldiers' kind hearts.

IN CAMP

At any period in history, camp life forms a prime example of the military mind at work, each moment of the day precisely regulated by a host of rules and restrictions. Indeed, without them anarchy would result, and soldiers always have to be kept busy to hinder them from getting into mischief.

Camps naturally varied both in size and purpose. During the off season as far as campaigning was concerned, the various armies went into winter quarters, being spread around the fortress towns in Flanders and in the surrounding villages. When the season opened an assembly camp was nominated for the army to gather, often in the vicinity of a major fortress. There the regiments would be reviewed, transport would be allotted and the initial issues of ammunition given out. This type of large entrenched camp was also used when an army was prepared to remain on the defensive. It would 'dig-in' under the guns of the fortress, posing a threat by its very presence and forcing the enemy to take notice.

On the march, nightly camps were purely open sites, but when an army proposed to spend several days in one place and in the presence of an enemy, elaborate entrenchments were thrown up, reminiscent of the Roman marching camps. The same applied during a siege with the lines of circumvallation and contravallation, but the same basic rule applied to all camps.

On the march, the quartermasters travelled with the advance cavalry guards and were responsible for selecting the camp site for the

Fig. 84. Encampment before Valenciennes (van der Meulen). This haphazard scene of camp life is far more real than the plans given in the books of the military theorists of the period.

following day and for marking it out. In well-known campaigning territory such as Flanders, this presented no great problem as the popular sites were well known in advance. In strange areas, however, suitable sites had to be reconnoitred.

Firstly, the site had to be large enough to house the size of force involved, had to have a good fresh water supply and be dry and well drained. It also had to have a good all-round view both for purposes of defence and to hinder desertion, and there had to be adequate supplies of fire wood, and forage for the horses. Once chosen, the camp was marked out with stakes and then the quarters of the various units were delineated by lines of turf cut out with spades. As the army arrived, men were detailed to guide the regiments into their particular section.

The above naturally represented an ideal to be aimed for, but at times it did work out in practice. Parker wrote of the march to the Danube:

'As we marched, commissaries were appointed to furnish us with all manner of necessaries for man and horse. These were brought to the ground before we arrived and the soldiers had nothing to do, but to pitch tents, boil their kettles, and lie down to rest. Surely never was such a march carried on with more order and regularity, and with less fatigue to both men and horse'.[15]

This was a summer march carried out by a small force under the direct guidance of Marlborough and his staff. Camping in poor weather and when the supply arrangements broke down was not so pleasant. Returning again to Blackader, he commented on one occasion: 'We are not able to stir out of our tents for bad weather, and are lying among the mire and dirt. . . . We had one of the severest storms I have ever seen, of hail, rain and wind. Most of our tents were beat down, and torn; and the hollow ways running like rivers.'[16]

In considering the above quotation it should be borne in mind that the soldiers only had the clothes they stood up in without any opportunity for a change (except perhaps a spare shirt), and that their only bedding was straw or greenery – no camp beds, waterproof sleeping-bags or even a couple of blankets. Only the

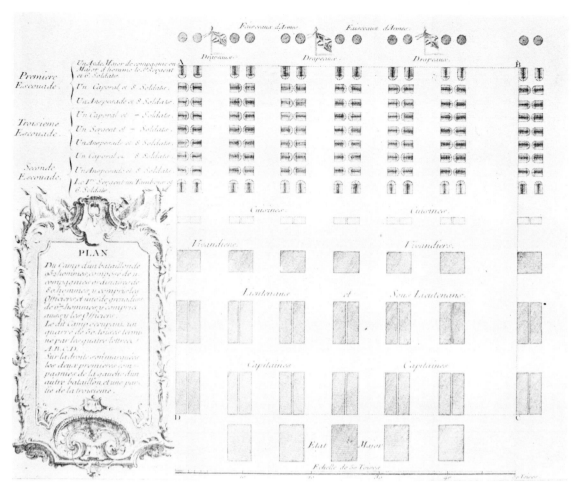

Fig. 85. The layout of an infantry camp from Puysegur. This shows the arms bells and the colours at the front. Unlike an English camp of the same period, the sutlers are positioned between the men and the officers.

wealthier officers were a little better off, having cloaks and proper beds.

Once on site, the various units proceeded to erect their tents in the allotted space according to a strictly laid-down pattern. An infantry battalion camped with the quarter-guard or picquet at the front, which was described as follows:

'. . . we have in every regiment of Horse and Foot, a certain number of men every day upon the Picket [sic] (as they term it). These are to be ready on every sudden occasion if an alarm happens by night or day to turn out at a minutes warning. They are to have their arms ready fixt and not to put off their cloathes but have naught to do unless an Alarm happens.'[17]

Behind the quarter-guard a free space was left for parades, followed by a group of tents for the drums and the colour party. The nco's and privates laid out their tents in six double-sided 'streets', and at the head of each was an arms bell. This was a bell tent in which the arms were stacked under guard for safety. Behind the men came the subalterns' tents and then the captains'. The senior officers together with the staff had a separate area, and right at the back were the horse lines, grooms' tents and the sutlers' lines.

A cavalry squadron camped in roughly the same way, except that the horses were tethered to picquets in lines parallel to the tent streets,

128

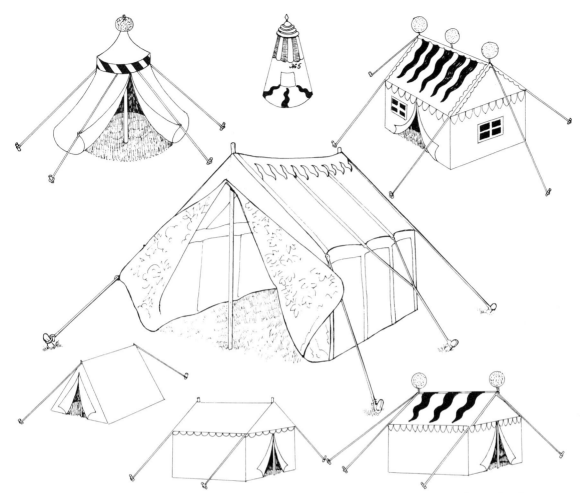

Fig. 86. Various contemporary tents taken from a 1689 painting. They vary from the three-man troop tent up to the senior officer's marquee. The coloured balls on the poles would seem to be an indication of rank.

so that they could be attended to at all times and were ready for mounting in an emergency.

The English slept three to a tent and the same men shared a common cooking pot. In the German armies, a tent *Kameradschaft* numbered five or six.

The men's tents were of the ridge type, supported by an upright at each end and a ridge-pole. The skirts were pegged to the ground. The 'arms bells' looked similar to the modern army bell tent, and the officers' tents were of the 'marquee' type – the higher the rank the larger the tent.

The artillery train had specific problems when in camp and thus a horde of special regulations applied. The guns were normally sited 3–400 yards in advance of the main army encampment, unlimbered and drawn up facing the direction in which an enemy was likely to approach. The worst hazard was fire, and the ammunition waggons normally occupied a roped-off enclosure well behind the guns where the craftsmen, guards and gunners had their tents. Indiscriminate fires were definitely not encouraged. It would seem that the Horse and Foot simply lit individual cooking fires, but other arrangements had to be made for the Train. Quite what these were is not clear, but an indication can be found in St Rémy's book where he illustrates a field kitchen made out of bricks and turf with a number of small hearths around the circumference. This may well have

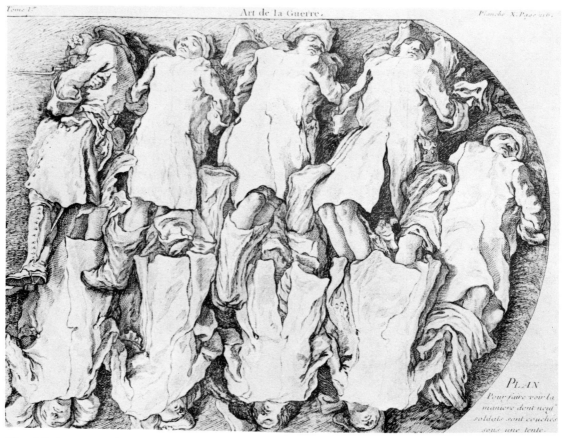

PLAN
Pour faire voir la maniere dont neuf soldats sont couchés sous une tente.

Fig. 87. Interior of French tent from Puysegur. To demonstrate the way in which nine men could be packed in. Note the sentry sleeping in his clothes.

been the French answer to the problem.

The above writer goes into great detail about Train parks, giving diagrammatic examples for various sizes of Train. He insisted on three officers and one conductor being on duty at all times, overseeing a complex organisation of guards and constantly making their rounds. In camp, the Train was also responsible for having a number of signal guns loaded at all times. These were fired for timekeeping purposes and also for giving warnings such as the general recall of outposts and foraging parties.

The whole question of forage was probably the most vital consideration when the army halted. The vast numbers of horses involved meant that it was impossible to simply turn them loose to graze. Instead, fodder had to be gathered, a time-consuming exercise which in turn emphasised the ever-present desertion problem. The various camp regulations tend to concentrate on the problem of guarding and regulating forage parties and to threaten dire penalties for anyone caught outside the camp without authority. Even water parties had to be accompanied by a sergeant. Half the army was guarding the other half!

No unit was allowed to cut more forage than for the number of horses on its actual establishment, and only one ration per animal was permitted. The official allotment for a battalion of Foot was 100 rations of grass or clover weighing 40 lbs per day. With reference to guards, Parker tells us: 'Upon all foragings, a strong detachment was sent out the night before, under the command of a general officer, to keep the foragers within bounds; to cover them from the enemy and to prevent irregularities and abuses.'[18] In a manuscript in the British

Museum there are details of a force of 1,000 infantry and 800 cavalry required to seal off a particular area.[19]

Daily life was precisely regulated. When Reveille was beaten, the men got up and tidied their tents ready for inspection by the officers. The previous day's guards were relieved at 8 a.m., and at 9 a.m. the chaplain said prayers at the head of the regiment. The rest of the day was spent in fatigues or training. Tents had to be opened to air every morning and arms were inspected twice weekly on pay days. Commanding officers were responsible for seeing that their men had twenty-four rounds of ammunition each with the 'cartouches well made'.[20]

In an age not noted for attention to matters of hygiene, care had to be taken of the latrines or 'houses of office'. Old ones had to be filled in and new ones dug every six days. Another rule stated 'that the camp always be kept clean, by making Houses of Office often' and officers were directed to see that the sutlers 'buried their filth'.

During the morning at 'orderly time', all general officers repaired to the Duke's quarters, where the orders for the day were issued to the Major-General of the Day, and the Adjutant-General was responsible for seeing that these were recorded, as well as keeping 'details of happenings'.

Once all duties had been performed, the men were able to seek solace in the sutlers' tents — usually of an alcoholic nature. 'Lights out', however, was at 9 p.m., and majors were responsible for making the rounds to see that the tents were empty. Tattoo was the drum signal that would be beaten, and this originates from the late seventeenth century when soldiers were often billeted in public houses or had to be dragged out from the tents of the sutlers. The word is a corruption from the Dutch *doe ten tap toe*, meaning shut off the tap.

At a higher level in the army, life was certainly more comfortable. We have seen some indication of the vast amounts of baggage carried by senior officers, and their tents must have made a magnificent display. When Marlborough was disgraced he was replaced as Captain-General by the Duke of Ormonde. Peter Drake describes the scene:

'. . . The Duke's kitchen tents already pitched in the orchard; thirty or forty cooks, scullions, turnspits and other servants, busy at their several employments, some spitting all sorts of flesh and fowl in season, others making pies and tarts, and others making fires and fixing boilers and ovens. . . . Then we went to see the dining tents, in the largest of which was a table of twenty-four covers, in another a table of eighteen and in a third one of twelve, all looking into each other, with a fourth for the music to play while His Grace was at dinner.'[21]

NOTES

1 Muller, J., *A Treatise of Artillery*. London. 1757. 83.
2 Scouller. 204. Quoting a Treasury document.
3 Churchill. Vol. I. 412 *et seq*.
4 Fortescue. R.A.S.C. 23.
5 Mérode-Westerloo. 181.
6 Scouller. 205.
7 Chandler. 'The March to the Danube.' *JSAHR*. 1972. 96.
8 Trevelyan. *Select Docs*. 112.
9 Duffy, C. *The Army of Frederick the Great*. David and Charles. 1974. 152–3.
10 Anon. *A System of Camp Discipline etc*. 11.
11 Parker. 57.
12 Susane. Vol. I. 271.
13 Kane. *The Wars of William etc*.
14 Blackader. 53.
15 Trevelyan. Op. cit. 112.
16 Blackader. Op. cit.
17 Noyes. Op. cit. Letter 3. *JSAHR*. 1959.
18 Parker. 121.
19 B.M. Trelawney Papers. Add MSS. 23, 624 f. 23.
20 Anon. Op. cit.
21 Drake. 293.

Fig. 88. Le boute-selle *(boots and saddles) after Guerard. The signal to mount being given by the trumpeter on the left.*

Fig. 89. A foraging party (Guerard). Cavalry troopers cutting and binding trusses of hay, surrounded by guard detachments.

LOGISTICS

It was a fact of life for early eighteenth-century armies that they could only march as far as they could carry their bread – it was this that determined their operating range. The normal factor was a four-day march followed by a one-day pause for baking or re-supply – 'it was imperative that provision should be made of at least a four days' supply of bread before beginning an advance.'[1]

During the Thirty Years War, armies had mainly relied on living off the land, constantly on the move as they consumed the supplies available in any one locality. As armies became larger in the seventeenth century, it became clear to governments that they could no longer rely on such methods, and that they had to lay down stocks in magazines at the opening of every season. Indeed, the campaigning season was determined by the availability of fodder on the ground for horses. Feeding the men put enough strain on the supply systems without having to cope with transportation of animal feed. Operating within the narrow confines of Flanders and the Low Countries would have been impossible without a logistic back-up.

If you operated in your own country or in the territory of an ally, it was obvious that you had to pay for what you consumed. Therefore, it was preferable where possible to subsist your army in enemy territory. Even then, however, the large-scale pillage of earlier wars was abandoned. The sensible way was to levy a contribution in cash or kind on the populace, who would

pay (albeit unwillingly) to avoid having the troops let loose on their property. In using this system, you deprived your enemy of the use of those supplies himself and robbed him of future tax revenue.

Wilful damage was seldom resorted to except as a punitive measure – Marlborough laid waste to Bavaria in 1704 in an attempt to force the Elector to come to terms.

Food (and drink) has always been something that has vitally affected the morale of any army and thus its ability to fight. A commander who ensured that his men were well and regularly fed usually had a good fighting force that would follow him without question. From the evidence available it would seem that Marlborough's men were, by the standards of the time, well supplied, which was seldom the case with many other armies of the period. The term 'starving' frequently appears in references to the Hapsburg armies, and even the French could not always provide a daily meat ration.

Feeding an army was an extremely complicated business – not only providing the food but also transporting it to the place where it was required. Therefore armies did not like to operate at more than 100 miles from their magazines, and it was a daring commander who cut himself off from his lines of communication – as Marlborough did in 1704 when he left the Netherlands to go to Southern Germany. Indeed, much of the manoeuvring that was carried out by armies of the period had

Fig. 90. Pillage. Tapestry by J. de Vos after L. de Hondt. A comparatively mild scene by the standards of the age.

the sole purpose of getting across the enemy's lines of communication and thus forcing him to react or retreat.

The logistical systems of the various nations had been built up over the years based largely on precedent and custom, and thoroughly bedevilled by graft and corruption on a massive scale. This was in no way considered unusual. In a period when many governments were unable to pay salaries to their officials, the latter were expected to enrich themselves on the side.

In the English army, a department known as the Commissioners of Victualling were responsible, a body answerable to the Treasury. In the field it was represented by Commissary-Generals who could be either military or civilian officials, plus a whole host of paymasters, muster-masters, clerks, commissaries, store-keepers, etc. The basic problem was that most governments were up to their ears in debt and perpetually short of actual ready cash. The

funds voted annually by a grudging Parliament went immediately for paying off arrears.

This lack of money was naturally compounded by crass incompetence. Basically, one can state that bread was the only item provided in kind by the government for consumption by the troops in the field during the Flanders campaigns. Payment came from the men's subsistence allowances and was deducted prior to issue, together with a contribution payable towards the cost of transport. The rest of their food was purchased in cash from the sutlers or the local inhabitants. The transport contribution, however, was never sufficient to cover the actual costs incurred. In addition, in a time of rising costs generally and of inflation, extra funds had to be provided from time to time in order to avoid shortfalls in troop feeding.[2]

The job of actually providing the bread was farmed out to civilian contractors, the main ones being the brothers Solomon and Moses

Medina, who in turn sub-contracted to other Jewish merchants based in the Netherlands. Theirs must have been a thankless task as their 'cash-flow' problems often brought them to the verge of bankruptcy. However, the prices they charged no doubt took into account the length of time they had to wait for their money. Marlborough did his best to see that they were paid, but the injustice was that it was the Medinas who conspired with his enemies in Parliament, resulting in his dismissal in 1711.

One ostensible reason for this was that he had received from them payments of $2\frac{1}{2}$ per cent on the bread contracts. This, however, was normal practice at the time and the same perquisite was voted by the same parliament to his successor, the Duke of Ormonde. The money was used to fund the secret intelligence service and there is no evidence to suggest that any of it wandered into Marlborough's pockets.[3] Other such payments 'on the side' were 1 per cent of all money passing through his hands, to Mr Sweet, the Paymaster at Antwerp.

The problem for the historian is to determine exactly what the troops received, as ration scales in documents possibly represented wishful thinking. It would seem, however, that the English troops fared far better than most, and were accustomed to a substantial diet. The subsistence rates give a clear indication of the pecking order in the army.[4]

The anonymous author of the *Recruiting Essay* published in 1707, wrote:

'The English ... are the best soldiers in the world so long as their beef and Pudding lasts ... that the people of other Countries can live harder than the English is not so much a Virtue in them, but from a necessity made habitual to them ... and there is no Nation under the Sun where the meaner people are bread [sic] up with such substantial nourishing foods as the English; Flesh, Fish, Bread, Butter, and Cheese, and malt Liquors being the General Diet of Her Majesty's labouring subjects.'

During the earlier wars of William III, the daily allowance in the field was 2 lbs of bread,

1 lb of meat or cheese and one bottle of wine or two of beer, and the same source quotes a whole list of items that commissaries were expected to provide.[5]

Where no civilian contractors existed, for example in such colonial outposts as Newfoundland, Minorca, Gibraltar, etc., the government had to ship supplies in bulk. This lack of suitable suppliers was keenly felt in the Peninsular theatre where the government was forced to take over the supply system. Strict instructions were issued to forbid plundering and local purchase was not permitted. Instead, the men had to buy from army stores, which were either obtained from the Portuguese or shipped out from England.

The French army would seem to have employed butchers and to have marched with its meat 'on the hoof', but there are no records of butchers on English army establishments. The provision of meat was the reponsibility of the sutlers – one 'grand' sutler per regiment and one 'petty' sutler per company or troop. Theirs was a hazardous but rewarding trade coupled with a high risk factor. Any sutler whose baggage hindered the movement of the army was liable to have his waggons overturned at the side of the road where the soldiers were permitted to plunder them. At battalion level it was the major's responsibility to control their activities and check their weights and measures. One can imagine, however, that any sutler caught cheating would have received little mercy from the soldiery.

The best account of sutlers and their operations can be gained from Daniel Defoe's book *The Life and Adventures of Mrs Christine Davis*, otherwise known as Mother Ross. She considered that a position right up the front with the 'forlorn hope' was well worth while, as any plunder needed only to be shared by a few.

During the devastation of Bavaria in the summer of 1704, she is on record as having said:

'We spared nothing, killing, burning, or otherwise destroying whatever we could not carry off. The bells of the Churches we broke to pieces, that we might bring them away with us. I filled two bed-ticks, after having thrown out the feathers, with bell metal, men's and women's clothes, some velvets and about a hundred Dutch caps, which I plundered from a shop; all of which I sold by the lump to a Jew, who followed the army to purchase our pillage, for four pistoles.'

This was being carried out in enemy territory, which was to a certain extent legitimate, as the laying waste of Bavaria had been ordered for political reasons. The risks of plundering, however, were obvious, as the Articles of War prescribed the death penalty for 'fleeing, abandoning post, going off for plunder, inducing others to do so – captured stores to be secured for Her Majesty.'[6]

De la Colonie's French grenadiers were real professionals. 'On their arrival at each camping ground it was their custom to go and seek for wood and straw, and under this pretext they set out in organised parties . . . to scout and pillage the country. . . . They brought in four of five hundred sheep at a time, besides cows and oxen, from pasturages far away from the camp.'[7] He goes on to say that the army butchers were in collusion with them. One interesting fact is that for a fee, payable to the army commander, the inhabitants could purchase immunity from being plundered. No wonder the French made themselves so unpopular and that the relatively disciplined English army was well received.

The French supply system was in the hands of the Louvois bureaucracy. The army operated from magazines laid down in winter and the various field commanders were accompanied by the *intendants*, government representatives responsible for all matters pertaining to supply.

Without vast subsidies from the Maritime Powers, the Hapsburgs would have been unable to take the field. The immense and unwieldy dominions of the Empire were totally incapable of financing their war effort and of feeding their troops. At the head of army administration was the Imperial War Council, but in many cases, court favour counted for more than competence in securing an appointment. During the early stages of the War of the Spanish Succession, contracts for supplies were placed through the 'Court Jew', Samuel Oppenheimer. In theory, the money came from grants voted by the Estates of the various Austrian hereditary lands, but this was never enough. Oppenheimer had the misfortune to die in 1702, owed 18 million gulden by the government, and the crash of his financial empire brought the state to the verge of bankruptcy.[8] Even Eugene's subsequent appointment to the presidency of the War Council did little to improve matters. 'The supply system in the Imperial Army was probably the worst among the Allies, and their soldiers had to put up with far worse conditions.'

Shortly before Blenheim, Marlborough wrote: 'The troops I have the honour to command cannot subsist without bread, and the Germans that are used to starve, cannot march without them.' Meat was a luxury for the Germans and, officially, attempts were made only to supply them with bread, biscuit, salt and some form of drink. This was issued in bulk from magazines that were supposed to have been laid down before the start of each campaign, but when supplies ran out, the troops were turned loose on the countryside or left to go hungry. Their lack of vitamins made them particularly susceptible to diseases such as scurvy.

It is clear that bread was regarded as the staple diet item in all armies. Soldiers could survive on this as long as it was supplemented by quantities of alcohol. The English were accustomed to beer, and when they drank large quantities of wine in Germany, dysentery became a problem. Spirits were regarded as being the best method of warding off the cold, especially when working in the trenches during a siege. In Flanders, Geneva gin was popular and cheap, although brandy is often mentioned.

The meat supply was regarded as important as it prevented the men from squandering their

Fig. 91. A camp scene. Tapestry by J. de Vos after L. de Hondt. Note the sutler's tent on the left, and the surround detail of military equipment.

money on drink. As it was of very poor quality, it could only have been boiled and made into stew or broth, supplemented with any vegetables that could be found. Matthew Bishop wrote that during the sieges of Ath and St Venant, they were issued with wheat and beans by the bushel. They boiled the beans and made dumplings from the wheat, which they thought 'good living'.

NOTES

1 Colonie. 345.
2 For a general review see Scouller 215 *et seq*. See also Perges, G.
3 Churchill. Vol. II. 894 *et seq*.
4 Scouller. Appendix H.
5 Walton. 695.
6 Scouller. 389.
7 Colonie. 173
8 McKay. 69.

Fig. 92. Camp scene by Marcellus Laroon. Note the ragged appearance of the men resting in the foreground.

Fig. 93. Sentries after Guerard. The sentry is still armed with a matchlock, while the sergeant wears a cuirass and carries a pike.

CLOTHING

By 1700, in Europe, royal authority vested in the sovereign had been asserted over the armed forces of all the major states. Although in many cases colonels continued to 'own' their regiments, these were no longer mercenary bands for hire to the highest bidder – the troops were subjects of a monarch or a state. Marlborough's soldiers fought under 'Corporal John' for a concept known to them as England and regarded themselves as Her Majesty's subjects. Patriotism was also a factor which had probably first appeared in Elizabeth's reign, and the inherent dislike of foreigners was a matter of popular appeal in England. We have seen that Sergeant Kite used dislike of the French in his opening appeal for recruits, and contemporary opinion regarded the 'Frenchies' as 'the most easily beat, and cowed of any people in the world'. No doubt their soldiers thought exactly the same of the English!

It follows from this that as the States became more and more involved in equipping and clothing their soldiers, there was a gradual drift towards uniformity, both as a means of identifying one's own troops and as a measure of economy made possible by bulk purchases of cloth and accoutrements. What a soldier wore was taking on the aspect of the King's (or Queen's) uniform rather than being a purely Regimental matter.

The first European nation to introduce uniformity was the Sweden of Gustavus Adolphus during the 1630s. The reason was that the Swedes had never really developed a feudal society in the Western European sense and thus the sense of obligation was to the State rather than to a man's superior in a feudal maze. Under Gustavus, the blue coats and breeches were introduced which were retained until well into the eighteenth century. Another early starter was Prussia whose infantry regiments all wore dark blue coats after 1691[1] and whose ammunition pouches all carried the royal monogram – although regimental arms were retained on officers' gorgets.

In England, some form of uniformity was introduced into the New Model Army, and at the Restoration the traditional red coat became more or less established, albeit with certain regimental variations.

It was in France, however, that state power and thus state control of the army became most firmly entrenched. Under the Louvois regime, colonels kept possession of their regiments, but *commissaires de guerre* were empowered to carry out inspections of clothing and equipment – a previously unthinkable action. In 1688, Louvois wrote to Martinet: 'Nor must officers be required to have all their [mens'] clothes with the same trimming, nor made at the same time, for this would be impossible. But we must not tolerate, no matter who the officers are, that their soldiers should be ill-shod or badly clothed.'[2] There were thus limits imposed on even the mighty Louvois and his royal master.

If actual uniformity was only hesitantly accepted, a similar *form* of clothing had become standard in the majority of the European armies; at least as an ideal to be aimed for. This consisted of the tricorn hat with the brim turned up on all three sides, a knee length button-through coat, breeches, stockings or gaiters and buckled leather shoes.

I say that this was an ideal, because implementation depended upon the organisation and funds available to provide it and standards differed widely. The worse off again, were the Austrians, where supplies of clothing and ammunition were in the hands of Jewish contractors. Prince Eugene wrote from Italy to the Emperor in the winter of 1703 that his troops had received no pay since the previous winter and 'meanwhile the men are having to go naked'.[3]

In the English army it was the Colonel's responsibility to clothe his men using the services of a Regimental agent. The cheaper the clothing the greater the profit for the Colonel. The state gave an allowance for clothing and equipment and the men themselves were expected to maintain it from stoppages taken from their meagre pay – which naturally led to many abuses.[4]

OFFICERS' CLOTHING

As far as officers were concerned, the lack of standardisation and uniformity is baffling, and the only solid evidence has to be gleaned from paintings and tapestries. However, one should not deduce from ceremonial portraits that senior officers wore suits of armour in battle! It was purely a convention to have oneself painted in armour with one hand negligently laid on a plumed helmet. Both in war and peace, officers were responsible for clothing themselves, although Regimental colonels could impose some sort of uniformity on their subordinates. Staff officers and generals could please themselves, and in a colourful age, their clothing often resembled the court attire of the period.

One distinguishing mark of the officer was the full bottomed wig, which started to go out of fashion in 1714. On their heads, they wore the standard black tricorn felt hat, the brim of which could be decorated with gold lace fringes, feathers, etc. One side could be pinned up with a gold wire loop around a button, and in some armies, cockades were worn.

Almost all wore a white lace cravat which frequently covered (in the case of the infantry) the gorget underneath. Coats were broad skirted and long, liberally decorated with gold or silver lace trimmings around the lapels, the buttonholes, seams, pockets and cuffs. Marlborough is always portrayed in the tapestries in scarlet coat and waistcoat with the turn-backs of the cuffs in the same colour, the whole liberally embellished with gold lace. The Laguerre frescoes at Marlborough House, however, show him after Blenheim in a plain red coat with a buff waistcoat.

In the group of staff officers surrounding him, there is again no discernible uniformity. One can see the grey coats of the Dutch, as well as blue and brown. Seeman's portrait of Armstrong, the chief engineer, shows him in the blue coat of the Ordnance. According to Laguerre, Eugene wore a cuirass at Blenheim, underneath a blue coat, whereas in other portraits he is depicted in various shades of red.[5] Colonie's regiment wore the traditional light blue of Bavaria, although he himself wore a red coat.[6] One could go on citing such examples.

For officers, a waist sash was part of their normal attire, although this item was sometimes worn over the shoulder. The sashes ended in large tassels or lace fringes, and in some cases had holes in the end through which poles could be inserted to form stretchers to carry the wearer off when wounded. Knee breeches were worn, often of contrasting colour, although Uncle Toby in *Tristram Shandy* had a pair in red plush. Mounted officers are normally shown wearing riding boots turned over at the top, but Marlborough obviously favoured buttoned gaiters or spatterdashes and buckle shoes.

For French Guards officers, the black and gold sash was a badge of rank, and shoulder knots of coloured ribbons were also worn by the French. All officers wore gorgets of brass

Fig. 94. Infantry clothing. Left, top to bottom, *officer's headdress, soldier's headdress, walking shoes.* Right, *officer's coat and sash. Note the position of the gorget.*

Fig. 95. Grenadier caps. (A) and (D) Bavarian. (B) a miner's cap. (C) Royal Irish. (E) French horse grenadier.

without emblems or devices, although the Guards had their's gilded, and as an exception the Swiss had silver ones and the other foreign regiments had steel gorgets.[7]

In order to provide some sort of guide, the following is a description of a junior officer of Foot in the English army, circa 1708.

Hat. Black felt with brim turned up on all three sides. Brim bound with silver lace and the left side fastened to the crown with a silver wire loop and button.

Neckcloth. Plain white with ends looped over in a simple knot, worn over a white collarless shirt.

Coat. Red, lined with buff and with the sleeves turned back to show the buff lining (facing). Front buttoned with silver buttons and the holes edged with silver lace. All seams lined with strips of silver lace as well as the pocket flaps and cuffs. Silver buttons on cuffs and pockets with silver lace loops. No collar to coat.

Gloves. Buff leather gauntlet type.

Sash. Crimson, knotted over left hip with fringed ends.

Waistcoat. Same colour as coat, edged with silver lace and with silver buttons.

Breeches. Red.

Stockings. Grey woollen fastened below the knee with a black garter. (Note: many regiments wore white pipe-clayed gaiters.)

Shoes. Black leather with long protruding tongue. Silver buckles.

SOLDIERS' CLOTHING

In the English army, the troops were clothed in a two-year cycle – a full outfit in the first year, and in the second, renewal of items subject to wear. The problem was that a recruit who joined in a 'small clothing year' might find himself without coat, waistcoat or breeches. In such a case, he would be issued with clothes taken from a dead comrade.

The off-reckonings from which clothing costs were to be met, did not take into account the effects of inflation, with the result that many regiments ran into debt with the clothing contractors – instead of making a profit the colonel found himself in difficulties. Often his only remedy was to cut down on the soldiers' subsistence in order to recoup himself. The *Recruiting Essay* gives the price of the first year as '£2/10/1' and the second as '14s. 4d.'[8]

Marlborough was certainly aware of the problem of regimental debts, rascally agents and the general decline from peacetime standards. In 1705 he entrusted the Board of General Officers with looking into the muddle, requiring them to provide answers and lay down standard patterns for clothing. In a report presented in 1708 the following was laid down as the basis for the 1708 campaign and for the following year:[9]

Line cavalry

First year	Second year
New lined coat	New lined coat
New waistcoat	New waistcoat
New laced hat	New laced hat
New boots	New boots
New gloves	New breeches
New horse furniture	New horse furniture
	New grenadier accoutrements

Dragoons

As for cavalry second year	As above

Foot

New coat – to be turned into a waistcoat for the following year	New coat
	Waistcoat made from previous year's coat
Kersey breeches	The same
Stockings	The same
Good strong shoes	The same
Two shirts and neckcloths	One of each
Well laced hat	The same

The above is an indication of what the soldier could expect to receive. Cavalry was naturally far more expensive to equip as such items as boots and harness were included, and the same applied to grenadiers. Note that no provision was made for any form of overcoat.

Such a scale, however, was purely theoretical. No soldier could go through a campaign with only one pair of shoes and stockings, and it is obvious that the poor soldiers had to fork out at regular intervals for replacements – or find a dead man of the same size.

Local purchase was frowned upon officially, but had been used in the last resort as in the famous case of Marlborough supplying shoes for the whole army on the March to the Danube. These were apparently delivered at Coblence and paid for via the Frankfurt bankers, the whole transaction having been arranged by Mr Davenport, Marlborough's agent.[10]

Chaplain Hare, however, who was present on the staff and must have known what was going on, said in his journal that the Duke wrote to his brother, General Churchill, at Heidelberg, ordering him to 'call the commanding officers of each regiment together, to cause them to make early provision of shoes and other necessities which would not be so easily found in an enemies Country [i.e. Bavaria]'.[11] From this one could infer that the colonels were at least in part responsibile for equipping their men on campaign.

An early eighteenth-century army must have made a brave sight on a review parade at the outset of a season, but after a few weeks the men would have looked like a bunch of tramps – marching in the mud and rain, and sleeping in their wet clothes in leaking tents. Much of the washing was done by female camp followers, and the men were ordered to wear their coats inside out when on fatigues. Inevitably the poor dyes of the time would have become faded and in spite of the bright colours in contemporary paintings, armies must in reality have looked somewhat drab. One answer to this problem was the use of field signs such as bunches of

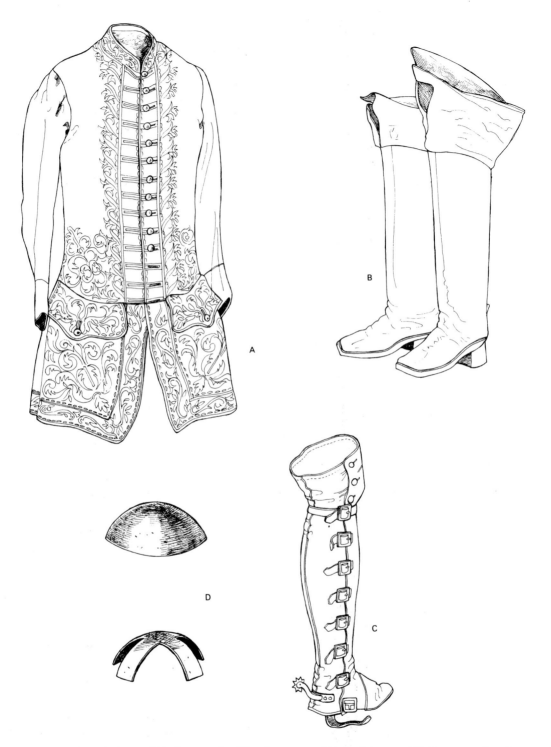

Fig. 96. Cavalry clothing. (A) German buff leather coat. (B) Jackboots. (C) Dragoon leggings and (D) two types of 'iron secret'.

greenery or straw worn on the standards and in hats.

Colonie, referring to the attack on the Schellenberg in 1704, wrote:

'I became aware of several lines of infantry in grayish-white uniforms on our left flank. I verily believed reinforcement had reached us. So, in the error I laboured under I shouted to my men that they were Frenchmen and friends. Having however, made a closer inspection, I discovered bunches of straw attached to their standards, badges the enemy are accustomed to wearing in battle.[12]

This rather gloomy picture contrasts oddly enough with the reports of contemporaries on the state of the English army in the field. They were undoubtedly the best and most regularly paid by early eighteenth-century standards. On the way to the Danube, the Elector of Mainz inspected Marlborough's cavalry, and when he came to the Guards drawn up on the right, he is said to have exclaimed that 'not only their order, but their cleanliness, and their Arms, Accoutrements, Clothes, Shoes and Linnen [sic]' were so admirable. Turning to General Churchill, he said 'certainly all these Gentlemen are Dressed for the Ball.'[13]

All European armies tended to take great care of the appearance of their Guards regiments, but much of the general standard of English line units must have been a result of the pride of the colonels and regimental officers. One aspect of this whole problem, however, remains somewhat of a mystery, and that is the private possessions of the troops.

We can see from paintings that all were clean shaven, but there is no evidence of razors being issued nor were barbers carried on establishments, Ordinary soldiers would not have had enough money to pay a civilian to shave them, so how did they manage their beards? We also do not know how they ate their food. 'Eating irons' were not apparently a standard issue item but at the very least some sort of plate, mug and cutlery would have been essential for every soldier. These were not well set up young men coming from home to join the army. Some would have brought private property with them, but the bulk were indigent vagrants or came straight from prison. Thus the contents of a soldier's haversack is unknown, and it is possible that he had to kit himself out with basic essentials as best he could. Many would have been smokers, requiring pipes and some means of lighting – probably tinder boxes – while others could well have carried writing materials. Items for cleaning their equipment are also lacking on official inventories but must have been provided from some source. The problem is that those who wrote memoirs were not interested in such mundane matters.

NOTES

1   Knötel und Sieg. 19.
2   Judge, H. *Louis XIV*. London. 1965. p. 17.
3   Henderson. 71–3.
4   See Scouller 126–63 for details of the system.
5   The Huchtenberg painting of the Battle of Turin and the portrait of Eugene at Peterwardein in the H. G. Museum in Vienna.
6   Colonie. 404.
7   Susane. 271.
8   See Scouller, Appendix I, for clothing scales.
9   Ibid. 151–2. Based on PRO Ordnance Letters. WO 46/6.
10 Churchill. Vol. I, 758.
11 Trevelyan. *Select Doc's*. 100.
12 Colonie. 191.
13 Trevelyan. Op. cit. 99. Quoting from Hare's *Journal*.

146

Fig. 98. Guidon and cornet carrying cavalry standards, and infantry ensigns. French engraving after Guerard.

Fig. 99. Cavalry trumpeter and kettle drummer after Guerard. Note the decorative stripes on their coats, and the banners on the instruments.

Fig. 97. A contemporary engraving of the standards taken by the Allies at Blenheim in 1704. Below is a list of the important prisoners.

MISCELLANEOUS SERVICES

MILITARY MUSIC

This is a subject about which comparatively little is known, and contemporary memoirs pay scant attention to musical matters. Strictly speaking, the musicians of the period were normally part of regimental establishments, which have already been referred to, but their specialist nature and their equipment merit separate consideration.

Music and warfare have always been closely associated, right back to the days of Joshua's feat of demolishing the fortifications of Jericho, with the aid of the regimental band. Basically, in the Marlborough period, military music had two aims — to assist in transmitting orders and to entertain the troops while marching.

It would seem that the origins of military music as we know it today grew up at the court of Louis XIV, whose composer, Lully, organised military bands and wrote music for them.[1] It was possibly at Versailles during his exile that Charles II gained a taste for such melodies, as musicians started to appear on the establishments of the Restoration army.

For the cavalry, the basic instrument was, as always, the trumpet. This was the keyless instrument rather like an elongated bugle that is still used today for blowing fanfares. They were made of brass and hung from the player's shoulder by ornate tasselled cords. The smarter regiments had beautifully embroidered silk trumpet banners decorated with the royal cypher or their colonel's arms.

Such instruments could only play the 'open' notes in one key, but there is some evidence that crooks of various lengths were inserted to alter the pitch.[2] This could well have enabled the trumpeters of a regiment to play together in harmony as a simple 'band'.

The other basic cavalry instrument was the kettle drum, still used by the Household Cavalry today. Such drums were of Turkish origin, and in Germany their use was restricted to élite units who had captured them in battle. Their symbolic value was equal to a standard, and the Blenheim Tapestry shows a grenadier guarding a captured flag and a pair of kettle drums.

Infantry drums were the normal cylindrical type but were much longer than the modern side drum — more the size and shape of a tenor drum in a dance band kit. They were made both with wood and metal shells, with the skins stretched on with cords that could be tensioned with leather tags. Although probably not general, there is some indication that snares were used to increase the output of noise.[3] The sides were painted, either with scenes or with emblems of a royal or regimental nature.

The other infantry (and dragoon) instrument of the period was the hautbois, or in modern terms, the oboe. The Baroque oboe bore little resemblance to its modern counterpart, consisting simply of a wooden pipe bored with a number of holes and a few keys for the bottom notes. The noise was produced by a reed similar to a modern bassoon reed, much broader than

Fig. 100. Detail of English kettle drummer and trumpeter from the Wootton painting of the Battle of Blenheim.

an oboe reed. In the English army they were only officially attached to the Foot Guards and the various dragoon regiments, where they made their appearance under Charles II. It is possible, however, that some regiments may have had 'unofficial' musicians who were paid for by the colonel. What is certain is that there were no military bands as such during the period.

Generally, musicians seem to have ranked in the pay scale as corporals and were clothed in corporals' quality cloth. By custom they were regarded internationally as non-combatants, although they carried short swords or hangers. In earlier times it had been the practice to break off the tips of their weapons to signify their status, but I have not been able to discover if this was still the case at the beginning of the

eighteenth century. They still seem to have functioned as heralds, as in his correspondence Marlborough frequently refers to having sent 'a trumpet' to arrange a parley.

As non-combatants, however, they were usually in the thick of fighting, accompanying their units into battle and being used for transmitting orders. Not all were brave, though, as Colonie observed. He commanded a Bavarian brigade at Ramillies, which came under intense cannon fire, whereupon he ordered 'flourishes upon our hautboys, to entertain us the while; but the booming of the guns so startled our musicians that they disappeared like a flash before anyone noticed it, and transported the melodious sounds of their instruments to some quarter where the harmonies were not quite so discordant.'[4]

149

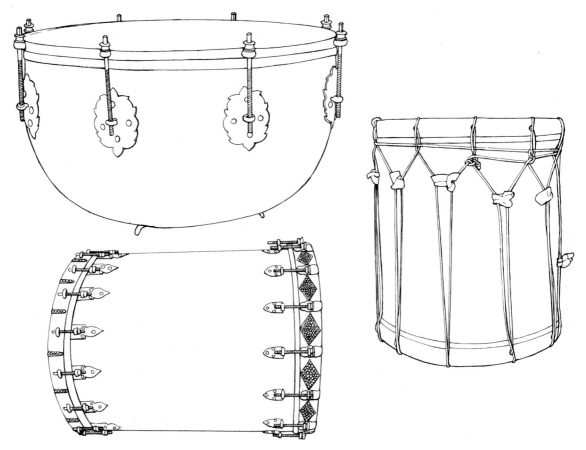

Fig. 101. *French kettle drum* (top left) *and two German side drums. One of the latter has screw tension plates while the other has the more usual leather toggles* (right).

The musicians in an English regiment were under the command of a drum-major, a rank which first made its appearance in the Guards of the Restoration army. He carried a staff (mace) as symbol of office, but it is doubtful if this was used at the time to indicate orders to the players. By the reign of Queen Anne, the drum-major became broadly established, and among his duties was the infliction of corporal punishment.[5] In addition, there was a Drum-Major-General carried on the headquarters establishment, but this office seems to have been a sinecure.

Another area of mystery is just what the musicians played. The main use of drums was for transmitting orders, and an authority writing in 1683 gave the main calls as – March, Troop, Battalia, Charge, Retraite, Batterie and Relief. We have already referred to the Tattoo as the signal for the end of the day, and the Chamade as a request for a parley. Kane, however, refers to such calls as March, and Halt, as well as Reveille, Assembly and General. Whatever the calls were named, what we do not know is how many beats and in which rhythm they were played. The same applies to the trumpet calls of the cavalry.

In a short section on the use of the drum in action, Kane wrote:

'Suppose the commanding officer should happen to be killed, the voice of him that supplies his place may be so different from the other's that it may occasion a confusion; whereas the drum is always the same and much easier heard and understood, . . . in the hurry of action when it is not possible for the voice to be heard, then the drum will be of the greatest consequence.'

150

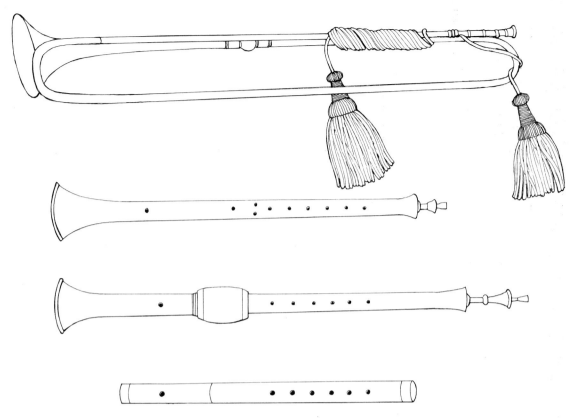

Fig. 102. Top to Bottom. *Cavalry trumpet (German), two different pitch hautbois and a fife.*

Fig. 103. The artillery train kettledrum carriage, drawn from the model in the Rotunda museum, Woolwich. The coachman sat on the small seat in the front.

Fig. 104. Infantry and mounted dragoon side drummers. Engraving after Guerard.

Soldiers the world over have always sung on the march, and Marlborough's were no exception. Although they had no bands as such, they had the drummers to beat time. Probably the most lasting song to come down to us is the *British Grenadiers*, written circa 1700. The third verse exactly sums up the duties of the grenadiers:

'When'er we are commanded to storm the palisades,
Our leaders march with fusees
And we with hand grenades.
We throw them from the glacis
About our enemies' ears,
With a ta ra ra, etc.'

The bastardisation of the French word *fusil* for flintlock in the second line refers to the fact that grenadier officers carried muskets instead of spontoons.

Another 'pop' tune of the period was *Lillibulero*, the words of which were Irish doggerel and violently anti-Papist. There was also the *Grenadiers March* and *Over the Hills and Far away*, both of which were referred to in the *Recruiting Sergeant* under the clear assumption that the audience knew the words.[6]

As is still the practice today, musicians could be distinguished by their dress, frequently wearing the regimental colour scheme reversed; their coats being the colour of the facings and the lining being the usual red. According to the generosity of the colonel, they would also have had a profusion of gold or silver lace. Drums were slung from leather belts either around the neck or over the right shoulder to rest on the left hip.[7]

The above remarks have applied to the Horse and Foot, but mention has already been made of the artillery drum carriage. It accompanied the Train in battle from the Irish campaign of 1689 until some time in the middle of the eighteenth century. This was a four-wheeled chariot pulled by six white horses and driven by a coachman on the box at the front. The drummer sat on a raised seat at the rear from where he could belabour two enormous drums. These were later used by Handel for performances of *The Messiah*, but were finally destroyed when the Tower Armouries caught fire in 1841, together with the carriage.

There is a replica of the carriage at the Rotunda Museum and the drum banners have

Fig. 105. A mounted musician playing a hautbois and an infantryman with a fife. Engraving after Guerard.

been preserved in the Officers' Mess at Woolwich.[8] In the Tower Armouries is a pair of kettle drums which survived the fire and which are said to have been captured from the French at Blenheim.

MEDICAL SERVICES

For most soldiers of the period, a good clean death from a well-aimed bullet was probably vastly better than a messy wound and to land up in the hands of the surgeons. Medical science was still in its infancy, antiseptics were unknown and the chances of surviving a serious wound were slender. If left on the battlefield, the wounded man could well have been robbed and stripped of his clothing and then have been murdered by the local peasantry. There were no identity discs or any system of burying the dead with decency. The corpses were piled up and burnt or heaved into pits filled with quicklime.

Efforts were made, however, to deal with the wounded, and the various regiments had a surgeon and his mate. Although civilians, they ranked as officers as the surgeon was paid at the same rate as a lieutenant. The employment of a surgeon was a matter for the regimental colonel and his pay was met by a monthly deduction of twopence from the mens' pay. Scouller wrote: 'It is safe to say that the medical services of Anne's armies were remarkable for mismanagement, brutality, inhumanity, and, possibly, corruption.'[9] This is a strong judgement, but it must be remembered that civilian doctors at the time were not much better. The fact is that there was nothing much to tempt a doctor into the service, so the army got the dross and the otherwise unemployable – qualifications were not required. After a campaign, the surgeon could simply be thrown out, owed money for his pay and reimbursement for what he had spent on drugs.

Not all were heartless butchers and there were some among them who genuinely cared for their patients. Quoting from the State Papers, Scouller cites a number of complaints from the staff of a naval hospital in Minorca about the conditions under which they were supposed to work.

The regimental surgeon was entitled to a

Fig. 106. After the battle. French school. Note the dead being stripped and the wounded man being attended to.

horse to carry his chest of equipment, and he could probably make a bit on the side through selling medicines. In the Blenheim Tapestry, there is a tiny vignette of a field dressing station and a surgeon at work. Carts were provided to carry the sick and wounded and orders issued to pad them with straw. This was either to give the unfortunate occupants a softer ride or to soak up the blood.

On the staff were the three personages known as the Surgeon, Physician and Apothecary to the Forces. They were appointed for a particular theatre and were supposedly responsible for the overseeing of the medical services. There was the ever-present problem of sickness and epidemics as well as wounds to be catered for. The West Indies were the graveyard of many fine regiments whose men fell victim to 'Yellow Jack', but Europe was also a pretty unhealthy place. In the undrained marshes of the Low Countries, soldiers died like flies from 'fever',

compounded by ill-cooked food and unaccustomed drink.

The lucky ones were those who served directly under Marlborough. It would seem that he had a genuine concern for the sick and wounded, and on the march to the Danube, Dr Hare wrote: 'His Grace thought it convenient to order a hospital to be appointed at this place [Mainz], as well for those few who were, as for others which might become sick and unable to march.'[10] Later, another hospital was set up at Heidenheim.

The responsibility for these hospitals during the Danube campaign was vested in Dr Thomas Law who was the Physician-General and the Duke's own doctor. Mr Hudson was Commissioner of the Hospital, and after the Schellenberg attack he established a hospital at Nördlingen. This was quartered in houses in the town and mainly staffed by the local population. However, the army widows were sent off there

Fig. 107. After the battle (engraving after Guerard). The mounted monk is offering the consolations of religion to the wounded, and as usual the dead are being plundered.

after Blenheim to act as nurses, and nine surgeons and their mates, two physicians and an apothecary were provided by the army. They had to care for some 4,000 wounded from the Schellenberg plus another 7,500 from Blenheim. How many of these survived the long journey in the jolting carts and arrived at the hospital is not clear. Neither is their subsequent fate or that of the widows who probably had to make their own way back to England.

Other armies were far worse off. In 1701, two waggons were sufficient to carry the whole medical supplies for Eugene's Imperial army operating in Italy, and the government was of the opinion that medicines were an expensive luxury.

Such conditions, however, were not restricted to the early eighteenth century, and the lot of the sick and wounded in the armed forces remained pitiable until the Crimean War and the activities of Florence Nightingale coupled with the power of Victorian public opinion and moral indignation, forced changes upon reluctant governments.

CHAPLAINS

In European history, religion and war have always been closely linked, and the armies of Queen Anne were provided with spiritual comfort – of the Protestant variety, naturally. Each regiment had its chaplain, who also ranked as an officer, being paid as a captain. A principal member of the army staff was the Chaplain-General, appointed by the Commander-in-Chief. In the case of Marlborough, this was Dr Hare whose journal has often been quoted.

It was this very literacy of the clergy that was so valuable in providing historians with many of the memoirs and letters of the period. Regimental chaplains, like the surgeons, were appointed by the colonels. Many of them were recruited from the unemployable, those without influence and the defrocked. No eighteenth-century clergyman was going to abandon a good living to follow the army.

Absenteeism was seemingly rife. Samuel Noyes, Chaplain to the Royal Scots, wrote from Flanders in 1703: 'The 26th [May] was

155

observed strictly as a fast by the Duke's order, a day or two before which His Grace required an account of what Chaplains were absent and the return was made 11 out of 24. They are either in England, Ireland or the Colonels' pockets.'[11] The latter phrase signified vacancies for which no incumbent had been appointed whereby the colonel could pocket the pay. Noyes went on to note that in July 1704 (at the time of the attack on the Schellenberg), there were only seven out of twenty-one chaplains present with the English army and none with the hospital at Nördlingen 'where there is most need'.

Divine service was held before going into battle, and prayers were supposed to be read daily to the men, but there is no evidence that the army was particularly devout. The hymn-singing Protestant troops of Gustavus Adolphus and the Commonwealth were already a thing of the past. However, given the fact that most armies of the period were made up from the dregs of humanity, there is no evidence to show that the Allied forces were particularly lax in their morals. Order was enforced by severe discipline, but the troops would have drunk and whored when they got the chance. Blackader continually lamented their lechery, swearing, profanity and thieving ways, but he was an odd man out in such a society. Marlborough's men were probably no better and no worse than soldiers of any period in history.

NOTES

1 Farmer, H. *The Rise and Development of Military Music*. London. n.d.
2 Ibid. 9.
3 Scouller. 386.
4 Colonie. 309.
5 Scouller. 100.
6 The music and words of the *Grenadiers March* are given in Palmer, R. *The Rambling Soldier*, Kestrel, 1977, pp 18–19. For contemporary songs see also the article by Farmer in *JSAHR*, 1950, and Weinstock, L. *The Songs and Music of the Red-coats*. Leo Cooper, 1970.
7 For drummers' clothing see article on the uniform of Erle's Regiment in *JSAHR*, 1968.
8 Article by Farmer in *JSAHR*, 1948, and op. cit.
9 Scouller. 235.
10 Trevelyan. *Select docs*. 98.
11 *JSAHR*, 1959.

APPENDIX

MISCELLANEOUS FIREARMS

Although the flintlock musket was the standard infantry weapon along with its shortened cavalry equivalent, the carbine, and one or two other firearms were available at the time. Some of these were used by the various armies of the period to a strictly limited extent, while others never got past the experimental stage. I discuss them briefly below as an indication of certain alternatives that were available and to show the way in which inventors' minds were working.

THE BLUNDERBUSS

In essence, this was a shortened carbine with the end of the barrel drawn out into a trumpet shape. They seem to have been popular with coachmen in the days of highwaymen, but they were also used by the military. The name probably comes from the German *donner-büchse*, which literally means 'thunder box' and which was most appropriate in the circumstances! However, as is the case with most weapons of the period, we come up against further name problems. A blunderbuss was probably the same as a musketoon, corrupted from the French *musquetoon*, which in turn could also mean a carbine.

It is probable that the true blunderbuss/musketoon was a large calibre short-barrelled weapon designed to discharge a scatter of small balls over a short range – the eighteenth-century equivalent of a sawn-off shotgun! They were issued to the navy in the latter part of the seventeenth century and would have been very suitable for close-quarter fighting on the decks of a ship.[1]

A further complication is that the French had a regiment of cavalry called the *Corps de Carabiniers*, who were not armed with carbines as their name suggests, but carried blunder-busses.[2]

RIFLES

In examining the musket we have seen that the inherent lack of accuracy resulted from the irregular travel of the ball along the barrel. The aim of rifling was to impart a controlled spin to the ball, and this technique was well known as early as the sixteenth century.

By the early eighteenth century, rifles were popular for hunting, and a target the size of a hand could be hit at a range of 80 to 100 paces. Their main defect was difficulty in loading, giving a rate of fire of only one round every three minutes. In practical terms, this meant that they were useless for military purposes within the frame work of early eighteenth-century tactics, besides which they were expensive to produce and required some expertise in handling.

However, some rifles were used in the Brandenburg/Prussian army, appearing for the first time in 1674.[3] These were hunting weapons brought in by peasants who had been called up for service, but the use of rifles on a regular basis came in the middle of the century when Frederick the Great formed special *Jäger* units.

These early German rifles were known as *Pflasterbüchsen* on account of the loading method, and were short-barrelled flintlock muzzle-loaders rifled with eight grooves. As the rate of bore wear was excessive, the grooves had to be frequently recut, which led to a great variety of calibres. Thus the riflemen could not use prepared cartridges and had moulds to cast their own bullets – which had to be enlarged with sandpaper after each rebore.

To load, the soldier took the weapon between his knees and poured in the charge from his powder flask. After this he laid the 'plaster' made of greased cotton or wool across the muzzle and on top of this he placed the bullet, as near as possible the same calibre as the weapon. Then he took a mallet which hung from a strap on his pouch and hammered the ball into the muzzle so that the 'plaster' wrapped itself around it. The next stage was to reverse the mallet and stuff the ball even further down with a few sharp blows. Only then could the ramrod be used, which needed great strength, especially after the bore became well encrusted with powder deposits. To test if the bullet was fully home against the charge, the riflemen bounced the ramrod in the bore a few times, checking to see if it sprang back to its original position.

GRENADE GUNS

Once the grenade became popular as a weapon, it was logical that inventive minds should turn their attention to mechanical methods of throwing them. It is not clear to what extent they succeeded, but the Tower Armouries collection has a number of such devices.

As early as 1681, a certain John Tinkler produced 'a new way of shooting Hand-granadoes out of small Morterpeeces' and a number of these were ordered shortly afterwards. The Tinker gun was a dual purpose weapon, the front part being a normal flintlock carbine. The butt, however, included a hollow cup designed to take a grenade when the butt plate was folded down. The actual lock was cunningly adapted to fire a charge in either direction.

The grenade would be placed fuze downwards in the cup and was ignited by the flash from the explosion of the charge. Such a device would have been difficult to fire by hand, and Grose states that it would have been fixed to a stick when throwing grenades.[4] Later types of grenade gun featured a normal musket to which a cup was fitted at the muzzle end, held in place by a bayonet clamp. These could naturally have been aimed and fired from the shoulder.

PARAPET GUNS

These were the direct descendants of the late mediaeval swivel guns and were used in fortresses. There were two basic types – the blunderbuss, which fired a charge of small balls as an anti-personnel weapon, and the rifle. The latter used the 'plaster' principle described above and were extremely effective for picking off senior officers who might be inspecting the siege works.

Parapet guns were mounted in forks which could traverse and which also helped to absorb the recoil. The rifled types had ranges of up to 500 yards, and were served by a crew of two or three men.

THE PUCKLE GUN

Ever since the gun had been discovered, inventors had been busy trying to devise means of increasing rate of fire. The obvious solution was the multi-barrel weapon, but these suffered from excessive weight for easy hand use. In the seventeenth century, the principle of the revolver was discovered, but the technology of the time was not up to producing a sufficiently gas-tight seal between the barrel and the various chambers. Anyway, such weapons would have

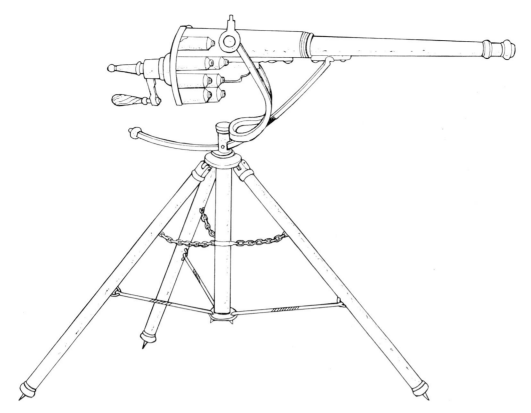

Fig. 108. The Puckle gun. Mounted on a tripod, this drawing shows the revolving magazine and the operating handle.

been far too espensive for troop issue and could only have been of interest to wealthy officers as personal weapons.

Another seventeenth-century idea was to load a number of charges one on top of each other in the barrel of a musket and to touch off the front one first. The explosion of this would start a chain reaction as the flash spread backwards, igniting the others one by one. Fine in principle, but once started could not be stopped. Besides, once it was empty, such a weapon would have taken quite an amount of time to reload.

However, ingenuity was not dead, and in 1717, James Puckle introduced his prototype machine-gun to the Ordnance, patenting it the following year.[5] This weapon, preserved at the Tower of London, looks remarkably modern. Essentially, the Puckle gun was mounted on a tripod and had a calibre of just over one inch. The magazine was a brass cylinder with a varying number of chambers which could be revolved against the fixed barrel by means of a crank handle. This also served to screw the cone-shaped chamber ends into the counter-sunk breech in order to form a tight seal.

The Board of Ordnance, however, were unimpressed and the British Army had to wait quite some time for its first issue of machine-guns.

NOTES

1 Blackmore. *British Military Firearms*. 32.
2 Chandler. *The Art of Warfare*. 33.
3 Eckhardt-Morawietz. 74–80.

4 Grose. 360. Blackmore. 35.
5 Blackmore. Op. cit. 237 et seq.

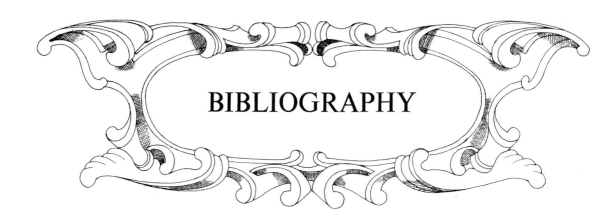

BIBLIOGRAPHY

The following is a list of books which have been consulted and which have a bearing on the subject. It does not include all the biographies of Marlborough and other generals, and works concerned solely with the campaigns have been omitted. Unless otherwise stated, place of publication is London.

1   *Primary Source*
    Murray, G., ed., *Letters and Dispatches of the Duke of Marlborough, 1845*.

2   *Contemporary Memoirs*
    Bishop, Matthew, *The Life and Adventures of, written by himself*, 1744.
    Blackader, Lt-Col. J., *Diary* (1700–1728), ed. A. Crichton, Edinburgh, 1824.
    Colonie, de la, *The Chronicles of an Old Campaigner*, trans. Horsley, 1904.
    Deane, Private John, *A Journal of the Campaign in Flanders MDCCVIII*, 1846.
    Drake, Peter, *Amiable Renegade, The Memoirs of Captain Peter Drake, 1671–1753*, Stanford University Press, 1960.
    Hare, *Journal,* British Museum, add. MS 9114 and quoted in Trevelyan, q.v.
    Kane, Brig.-Gen., *The Wars of William III and Queene Anne*, 1735.
    Millner, Sgt J., *Journal*, 1733.
    Parker, Capt. R., and Mérode-Westerloo, Comte de, ed. David Chandler, 1968.

    Scot, John, 'A Private in the Scots Brigade 1701–1711', in Ferguson, J., *The Scots Brigade in the Netherlands 1572–1782*, Vol. III, 1901.

3   *Contemporary Fiction*
    Defoe, Daniel, *The Life and Adventures of Mrs Christian Davies* (Mother Ross).
    Farquhar, George, *The Recruiting Sergeant*.
    Smollett, Tobias, *Roderick Random*.
    Sterne, Laurence, *The Life and Opinions of Tristram Shandy*.

4   *Secondary Works*
    Andrzezewski, S., *Military Organisation and Society*, 1957.
    Anon, *A System of Camp Discipline, Military Honours and Garrison Duty and Other Regulations for the Land Force, Collected by a Gentleman of the Army*, 1757.
    Anon, *An Essay on the Most Effective Way to Recruit the Army, 1707*.
    Barnes, R. M., *A History of the Regiments and Uniforms of the British Army*, n.d.
    Barnett, Corelli, *Marlborough*, 1974.
    —— *Britain and her Army*, 1968.
    Belidor, B. F. de, *La Science des Ingénieurs dans la Conduite des Traveaux de Fortification et d'Architecture Civile*, Paris, 1729.

Blackmore, H. L., *The Armouries of the Tower of London*, Vol. I, 1976.

—— *British Military Firearms, 1650–1850*, 1961.

Blomfield, R., *Sébastion le Prestre de Vauban*, 1938.

Carman, W. Y., *British Military Uniforms from Contemporary Pictures*, 1968.

Chandler, D., *Marlborough as a Military Commander*, 1973.

—— *The Art of War in the Age of Marlborough*, 1976.

Childs, J., *The Army of Charles II*, 1976.

Churchill, Winston S., *Marlborough, His Life and Times*, 2 vols, 1947.

Clark, Sir G., *War and Society in the 17th Century*, Oxford, 1958.

Duffy, C., *Fire and Stone*, 1975.

—— *The Army of Frederick the Great*, 1974.

Earle, E. M., ed., *Makers of Modern Strategy*, Princeton, 1944.

Eckhardt-Morawietz, *Die Handwaffen der Brandenburgisch-deutschen Heeres*, Hamburg, 1957.

Exercise for the Horse, Dragoon and Foot Forces, 1728.

Farmer, H. G., *The Rise and Development of Military Music*, n.d.

Ffoulkes, C., *Armies and Armament: An Historical Survey of the Weapons of the British Army*, 1945.

Fleming, H. K., *Der Vollkommene Teutsche Soldat*, Leipzig, 1726.

Fontaine, de la, *Les Devoirs Militaires des Officiers d'Infanterie et de Cavalerie*, Paris, 1672.

Fortescue, Sir J., *A History of the British Army*, Vol. I, 1932.

—— *The Royal Army Service Corps. A History of Transport and Supply in the British Army*, Vol. I, Cambridge, 1930.

Frischauer, P., *Prince Eugene*, 1934.

Fuller, J. F. C., *Armament and History*, 1946.

Funcke, L. and F., *The Lace Wars*, 2 vols, 1977.

Green, D., *Blenheim*, 1974.

Grose, D., *Military Antiquities respecting a History of the English Army*, 1801.

Hall, A. R., *Ballistics in the 17th Century*, Cambridge, 1952.

Hamilton, F. W., *The Origin and History of the Grenadier Guards*, 1877.

Hatton, R. M., *Charles XII*, 1968.

Henderson, N., *Prince Eugen of Savoy*, 1964.

Hogg, O. F. G., *English Artillery 1326–1716*, 1958.

Howard, M., *War in European History*, Oxford, 1976.

Hüttl, L., *Max Emanuel, Der Blaue Kurfürst*, Munich, 1976.

Janowitz, M., *The Professional Soldier – A Social and Political Portrait*, 1964.

Kamen, H., *The War of Succession in Spain*, 1969.

Kling, C., *Geschichte der Bekleidung, Bewaffnung und Ausrüstung des Königlich Preussischen Heeres*, 3 vols, Weimar, 1912.

Knötel, H. and Sieg, H., *Handbuch der Uniformkunde*, Hamburg, 1937.

Lawson, C. C. P., *A History of the Uniforms of the British Army*, 1940.

Lediard, T., *The Life of John, Duke of Marlborough*, 1736.

Lloyd, E. M., *A Review of the History of Infantry*, 1908.

Luard, J., *A History of the Dress of the British Soldier*, 1852.

McKay, D., *Prince Eugene of Savoy*, 1977.

Mollo, B. and J., *Uniforms of the Imperial Russian Army*, Poole, 1979.

Muller, J., *A Treatise of Artillery*, 1757.

Nef, U., *War and Human Progress*, 1950.

Palmer, R., *The Rambling Soldier*, 1977.

Parent, M. and Verroust, J., *Vauban*, Paris, 1971.

Pergés, G., *Army Provisioning, Logistics and Strategy in the Second Half of the 17th Century*, Budapest, 1970.

Peterson, H. L., *Round Shot and Rammers*, New York, 1969.

Pope, D., *Guns*, 1974.

Porter, Whitworth, *History of the Corps of Royal Engineers*, Vol. I, 1889.

Rogers, H. C. B., *The British Army of the 18th Century*, 1977.

Saint-Rémy, S., de, *Mémoires de l'Artillerie*, 2 vols, Amsterdam, 1702.

Saxe, M. de, *Mes Rêveries, Ouvrage Posthume de Maurice, Comte de Saxe*, 2 vols, Paris, 1757.

Schwenke, A., *Geschichte der Hannoverschen Truppen im Spanischen Erbfolgekrieg, 1701–1714*, Göttingen, 1862.

Scouller, R. E., *The Armies of Queen Anne*, Oxford, 1966.

Sturgill, C. C., *Marshal Villars and the War of the Spanish Succession*, Lexington, 1965.

Susane, L., *Histoire de l'Ancienne Infanterie Française*, Paris, 1849.

Taylor, F., *The Wars of Marlborough, 1702–9*, Oxford, 1921.

Teuber, C. O., *Die Österreichische Armee von 1700 bis 1867*, Vienna, 1895.

Trevelyan, G. M., *England under Queen Anne, Blenheim*, 1930.

—— *Select Documents for Queen Anne's Reign*, Cambridge, 1929.

Turner, E. S., *Gallant Gentlemen – a Portrait of the British Officer, 1600–1950*, 1956.

Various Authors, *Die Schlacht bei Minden 1759*, Minden, 1959.

Vauban, S. L. de, *A Manual of Siegecraft and Fortification*, trans. G. Rothrock, Ann Arbor, Michigan, 1968.

—— *Traité de l'Attaque des Places*, Paris, 1779.

Wace, A., *The Marlborough Tapestries at Blenheim Palace*, 1968.

Walton, C., *The History of the British Standing Army 1660–1700*, 1894.

Wilson, F., *The Uniforms of Marlborough's Wars*, 1970.

Wilkinson-Latham, R., *Swords in Colour*, Poole, 1977.

Weinstock, L., *Songs and Music of the Redcoats*, 1970.

Zimmermann, J., *Militärverwaltung und Heeresaufbringung in Österreich bis 1806*, Part III of *Handbuch der deutschen Militärgeschichte*, Frankfurt, 1965.

5 *Articles*

Akerman, J. Y., 'Notes on the Origin and History of the Bayonet', *Archaeologia*, XXXVII.

Chandler, D., 'The Campaign of 1704', *History Today*, Jan., 1963.

Farmer, J. G., '*The Great Kettledrums of the Artillery*' (*JSAHR*), 1948.

Francis, D., 'Marlborough's March to the Danube', *Journal of the Society for Army Historical Research* (*JSAHR*), 1972.

Ffoulkes, C., 'Notes on Early Military Bands', (*JSAHR*), 1938.

Johnston, S. H. F., ed. 'The Letters of Samuel Noyes' (*JSAHR*), 1959.

Scott, Sir S. D., 'On the History of the Bayonet', *Journal of the Royal United Service Institution*, vol. VI.

'The Dress of Erle's Regiment in 1704 and 1708' (*JSAHR*), 1968.

'Letters of the 1st Lord Orkney during Marlborough's campaigns', *English Historical Review*, April, 1904.

GLOSSARY

The following is a selection of the more common technical terms used in military literature of the early eighteenth century. Many of them are corruptions of foreign words and have several alternative spellings.

Abbreviations: F=French, G=German.

Abattis. A barrier of felled trees.

Arme-blanche (F). Cold Steel.

Avant-train (F). Limber.

Baldric (baudrière) (F). Fabric sword support.

Bandolier. Shoulder belt for carrying powder charges.

Blunderbuss. Short barrel large bore musket firing small shot.

Bomb. Explosive shell fired from a mortar or howitzer.

Boor. A corruption of the Dutch word *boer* meaning a peasant.

Brevet. Temporary commissioned rank.

Brigade. A tactical grouping of battalions.

Budge-barrel. A ready-use powder container kept beside a gun.

Caisson. Ammunition waggon.

Calibre. The diameter of a gun barrel.

Canister. Artillery projectile consisting of a container filled with small balls.

Cannon of battery. A siege gun.

Canteen. An officer's drinking flask.

Capsquare. Metal clamps passing over the trunnions of a gun to allow it to swivel on the carriage.

Carabinier (F). French élite cavalry armed with blunderbusses.

Caracole. The turning of a cavalry unit through 180 degrees.

Carbine. A short barrel cavalry musket.

Carcass. An incendiary projectile.

Carrée (F). A defensive square formed by infantry.

Cartouche (F). A cartridge. Sometimes used in English.

Cascabel. The knob (often decorated) at the breech-end of a cannon.

Case-shot. See Canister.

Ceinturon (F). Sword belt.

Chamade (F). The signal for a parley.

Cheval-de-frise (F). An obstacle of wooden spikes set into a pole.

Chevaux-légers (F). Light horse.

Coehoern. A small mortar.

Commissary. An official responsible for stores, etc.

Conducteur (conductor). A civilian official accompanying an artillery train.

Cornet. A cavalry subaltern.

Corps d'élite (F). Guard or other élite troops.

Coup de main (F). A surprise attack.

Course (F). A cavalry raid.

Cuirass. Body armour comprising back- and breastplate.

Cuirrassier. Cavalry troops wearing the above.

Culverin. 16 pounder cannon.

Curfew (Couvre-feu) (F). Time at which troops or civilians had to be off the streets in a fortress town.

Demi-cuirass. Breastplate.

Demi-culverin. 9 pounder cannon.

Division. A tactical sub-division of an infantry battalion.

Dolphin. Decorative lifting handle on a gun barrel.

Drabants. Swedish household cavalry.

Dragon. Short barrel carbine with full musket bore.

Dragoon. Mounted infantry.

Drake. Small cannon.

Enfilade. To fire along a line of trenches.

Ensign. Infantry subaltern, standard bearer.

Evolutions. Drill movements carried out by bodies of troops.

Facings. Contrasting colour used on uniforms for cuffs, pocket flaps, lapels, etc. Jacket lining colour.

Faggot. A man used to fill-in at a muster parade.

Falcon. $2\frac{1}{2}$ pounder cannon.

Falconet. 1 pounder cannon.

Fantassin (F). Infantryman.

Fascine. Bundle of brushwood for filling ditches, etc.

Feu-de-joie (F). Three shots fired from every cannon and musket as a sign of celebration.

Firelock. A flintlock musket.

Fireworker. Man responsible for the filling of mortar bombs.

Firing. Infantry battalion sub-division for delivery of musket fire.

Flam. A roll of drums.

Foraging. The gathering of feed for horses.

Forlorn Hope (enfants-perdus) (F). Storming party, or rearguard when retreating.

Frizzen. The plate on which a flint was struck to create sparks.

Frog. Bayonet holder suspended from sword belt.

Furniture. (1) The metal fittings on a musket or other firearm.

　　(2) Horse harness and saddlecloth.

Fusil (F). Flintlock musket, also used in English.

Fusilier. Infantry originally formed to guard artillery train.

Gabion. A wicker basket filled with earth – used to build breastworks, etc.

Galloper. A light gun-carriage pulled by a single horse.

Gambadoes. Heavy riding boots.

Gens d'armes, Gendarmerie. French élite cavalry unit.

Giberne (F). Cartridge pouch.

Gorget. Metal plate worn round neck as a sign of commissioned rank.

Grenade (grenadoe). Small bomb thrown by hand.

Grenadière (F). A grenade pouch.

Guidon. A cavalry standard.

Half-cock. The 'safe' position on a musket whereby the cock was pulled back to half-tension and held by a catch.

Halberd. Staff weapon carried by sergeants as a sign of rank.

Handspike. Heavy lever used for moving the trail of a gun carriage.

Hanger. Short infantry sword.

Hautbois. Original name for an oboe.

Horse (the). General name for cavalry.

Howitzer. A mobile mortar mounted on a carriage.

Hussar. A light horseman of Hungarian origin.

Intendance (F). The French supply authorities.

Invalid. Military pensioner, possibly serving in a fortress.

Kameradschaft (G). A small group of men sharing a tent.

Knapsack. Infantry haversack.

Levy money. Sum paid to a recruit to persuade him to enlist.

Limber. Two-wheeled support placed under the trail of a gun carriage to enable it to be moved.

Linstock. Wooden pole to carry a length of match for firing artillery.

Magazine. Storage place for supplies and/or ammunition.

Maison du Roi. French household cavalry.

Maréchal-des-logis (F). A quartermaster.

Marquee (from marquis) (F). A large tent.

Match. A piece of cord soaked in chemical used for igniting powder charge in a gun.

Matchlock. A gun lock incorporating the above.

Matrosse. An assistant gunner.

Mêlée (F). Close quarter cavalry combat.

Minion. 3 pounder cannon.

Mortar. A high-angle gun fired from a fixed bed.

Mousquet (F). A matchlock musket.

Mousquetaires. French élite unit.

Officier-pointeur (F). Officer responsible for aligning guns.

Palisade. A fence of stakes used to create an obstacle.

Pan. Receptacle for the priming charge in a hand gun.

Parallel. Siege trench.

Park. Camping area for the train.

Partridge. Slang name for canister or case shot.

Picquet. Guard detachment.

Pierrier (F). A type of mortar used for firing stones.

Picqueting. Form of punishment.

Pivot man. Man around which a cavalry unit wheeled.

Platoon. Tactical sub-division of an infantry battalion for fire control purposes.

Point blank. The range of a gun with the barrel neither elevated nor depressed.

Port-fire (Port-feu) (F). Holder for a length of quick-match.

Push of pike. Close combat fighting.

Postures. Drill movements.

Poudrière (F). Flask containing priming powder.

Quadrant. Instrument for determining the angle of elevation of a gun barrel.

Quoin (coyne). Wooden wedge for controlling elevation of a gun in its carriage.

Regimental piece. Light gun attached to infantry units.

Ricochet fire. Causing cannon shot to skip along the ground.

Robinet. Small cannon.

Roquelaure (F). A cloak.

Running the gauntlet (gantlope). Form of punishment.

Saker. 5 pounder cannon.

Sap. Siege trench driven forward from the parallels.

Sapper. One who dug the above.

Schweinsfedern (Swedish feathers). An infantry defence of pointed stakes placed in front of a position.

Secrets. Iron skull-cap worn under a hat.

Snaphance (Schnaphahn) (G). Early form of flintlock.

Spatterdash. A gaiter or leggings.

Spike. To disable a gun by driving a metal spike into the touch-hole.

Spontoon (Esponton) (F). Staff weapon carried by junior officers.

Squadron. Tactical sub-division of a cavalry regiment.

Subject troops. Troops of British nationality.

Subsistence. Money paid to troops for the purchase of food.

Sutler. Trader selling food and drink to troops.

Tattoo. 'Lights out' time in camp. Corrupted from the Dutch.

Tinboat men. Pontoon troops.

Tin-men. Fuze makers.

Tompion. Stopper for gun muzzle to keep out rain and dirt.

Trabans. Austrian household cavalry.

Trail. The rear part of a gun carriage that rested on the ground.

Train. The artillery, baggage and engineers of an army.

Train-grease (sope – tallow). Lubrication for cart wheels and axles.

Trooper. A cavalryman.

Trunnion. Lugs cast on to the point of balance of a gun barrel to allow it to swivel in its carriage.

Tumbril. Two-wheeled cart.

Valise. Container for personal possessions issued to cavalry.

Vent. Another name for the touch-hole of a cannon or mortar.

Vivandier (F). Sutler.

Widow's men. Non-existent men carried on a battalion establishment, whose pay provided pensions for widows.

Wild Geese. Irish émigrés in foreign service.

Windage. The gap between barrel and shot in a gun.

Wooden Horse. Form of punishment.

Worm. Bore scraper tool.

PERMANENT FORTIFICATION TERMS

Approaches. Trenches dug towards a fortress to enable the attackers to reach it under cover.

Banquette. Infantry fire step behind a parapet.

Bastion. A projection from the main rampart consisting of two flanks and two faces.

Batardeau. A dam to retain water in a wet ditch.

Berm. A ledge at the base of a rampart.

Bonnet. A triangular work at the salient of a ravelin.

Boyau. A communication trench.

Breastwork (Épaulement). A parapet to protect troops or guns.

Caponnière. A passage way protected on either side by breastworks, running from the enceinte to an outwork.

Casemate. A vaulted chamber.

Cavalier. An elevated battery position inside a work.

Chemin des rondes. A sentry path around the revetment of a rampart.

Circumvallation. (Lines of). Works constructed to defend a besieger's camp against a relieving army.

Citadel. A self-contained fort separate but usually attached to a town enceinte.

Cordon. A continuous rounded coping at the top of a masonry revetment.

Counterfort. An interior buttress.

Counterguard. A work in the ditch in front of the faces of a bastion.

Counterscarp. The retaining wall on the outside of a ditch.

Countervallation (Contrevallation) (Lines of). Defences thrown up by a besieger facing a fortress.

Covered Way. An infantry position round the outer edge of a ditch.

Crownwork. An outwork consisting of two long flanks and a front with a bastion and two demi-bastions.

Curtain. The length of rampart between two bastions.

Cunette. A drainage ditch sunk into the floor of a main ditch.

Deblai. Spoil excavated from the digging of a ditch.

Embrasure. An opening through which a gun can fire.

Enceinte (The body of a place). The main perimeter of bastions and curtains.

Enfilade. Fire coming from the flank in such a way that it can be directed along a section of the fortifications.

Face. Two forward sides of a work that meet to form a salient.

Fausse-Braye. A low rampart in the ditch below a main rampart.

Flank. The side of a work.

Flanker. A battery in the flank of a bastion.

Glacis. The bare downward slope from the works of a fortress towards the open country.

Gorge. The rear wall of a work.

Guerite (Éschaugette). A sentry-box on a bastion or curtain.

Hornwork. A work consisting of two long sides and a front of two demi-bastions.

Merlon. The solid length of parapet between two embrasures.

Orillon. The projecting shoulder of a bastion behind which a flanker battery can be protected.

Palisade. A fence made of pointed stakes.

Parados. An earth parapet to protect the rear of an infantry or gun position.

Parallel. A siege trench dug parallel to the front of a fortress to be attacked.

Place of Arms (Place d'Armes). An enlargement of the covered way where troops can be assembled for a sortie.

Rampart. Piled earth to form the main obstacle to an enemy.

Ravelin (Half Moon or Demi-Lune). A triangular work in the ditch in front of a curtain.

Redan. A work consisting of two faces and open at the gorge.

Redoubt. A small detached work or fort.

Re-entrant. An inward facing angle.

Remblai. The spoil piled up to form a rampart.

Retrenchment. An inner line of defence often built behind a breach.

Revetment. A retaining wall.

Salient. An angle facing outwards.

Sap. A siege trench.

Scarp (Escarp). The inner wall of a ditch.

Talus. The rearward slope of a rampart.

Tenaille. A low work in the ditch in front of a curtain.

Terreplain. The gun position on top of a rampart.

Trace. The ground plan of a fortification.

Traverse. A mound of earth at right-angles to the alignment of a work to protect the defenders from enfilade.

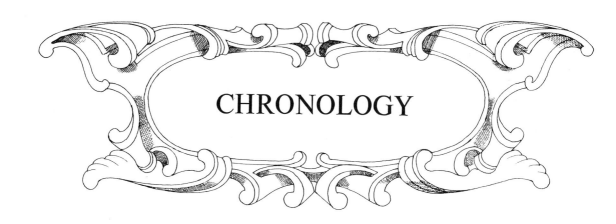

CHRONOLOGY

Date	General and Political	Marlborough's Campaigns	Other Military Events
1650	John Churchill born		
1663	Prince Eugene born		
1700	Start of Great Northern War		Battle of Narva
1701	French occupation of Dutch garrisoned fortresses in the Netherlands Sept. Death of James II		
1702	8 Mar. Death of Will. III. Accession of Anne. Marlborough appointed Capt.-General. 15 May, war declared against France	Siege of Liège, June–Oct. Siege of Roermond, Sept.–Oct.	Battle of Friedlingen, 14 Oct.
1703	Start of Hungarian rebellion	Siege of Bonn, April–May Battle of Erckeren, 30 June	First battle of Höchstädt, 20 Sept.
1704		Battle of the Schellenberg, 2 July Blenheim, 13 Aug. Siege of Landau, Sept.–Oct. Siege of Traben-Trarbach, Nov.–Dec.	Capture of Gibraltar
1705	Death of Emperor Leopold	Battle of Elixhem, 18 July	Battle of Cassano, 16 Aug. Siege of Barcelona, Sept.–Oct.
1706		Battle of Ramillies, 23 May Siege of Ostend, June–July Siege of Menin, July–Aug. Siege of Dendermonde, Aug.–Sept.	Battle of Turin, 7 Sept.
1707			Battle of Alamanza, 25 April Siege of Toulon, July–Aug.
1708		Battle of Oudenarde, 11 July Battle of Wynendael, 28 Sept. Siege of Lille, Aug.–Dec.	
1709		Battle of Malplaquet, 11 Sept. Siege of Tournai, June–Sept.	Battle of Poltava, 9 July

Date	General and Political	Marlborough's Campaigns	Other Military Events
1710	Fall of the Godolphin ministry in Britain. Harley appointed	Siege of Douai, April–June	
1711	Death of Emperor Joseph. Marlborough dismissed from all offices in December	Passage of *Ne Plus Ultra* Lines, 5/6 Aug. Siege of Bouchain, Aug.–Sept.	
1712			Battle of Denain, 24 July
1713	Signature of Treaty of Utrecht		
1714	Death of Anne Marlborough reinstated in office		
1715	Death of Louis XIV		
1721	End of Great Northern War		
1722	Death of Marlborough in June		
1736	Death of Prince Eugene		

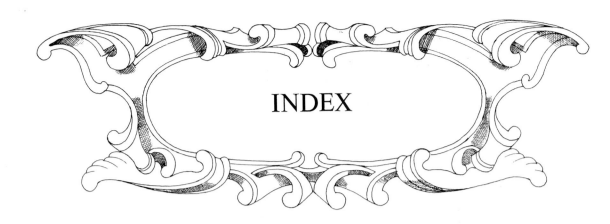

INDEX